D1233499

STRATIGRAPHY

STRATIGRAPHY

AN INTRODUCTION TO PRINCIPLES

BY

D. T. DONOVAN

London

THOMAS MURBY AND CO
40 MUSEUM STREET

George Allen & Unwin Ltd
40 Museum Street, London, WC1
are the proprietors of
Thomas Murby & Co.

PRINTED IN GREAT BRITAIN
in 11 point Times Roman type
BY C. TINLING AND CO., LTD
LIVERPOOL, LONDON AND PRESCOT

PREFACE

I have sought to give an account of the principles of correlation and classification of the sedimentary rocks with brief reference to their history. In describing terminology and classification I have confined myself to practice in English-speaking countries, and have noted some of the chief differences between British and North American usage. Some controversial matters are treated briefly or omitted. It would have been wrong to ignore past and present differences of opinion, but equally inappropriate to give detailed accounts of them in an elementary textbook.

Some countries have codes of stratigraphical practice and others are debating the introduction of codes. Furthermore, past International Geological Congresses have from time to time discussed stratigraphical usage, and the Nineteenth Congress (1952) set up a Subcommission on Stratigraphic Terminology which hopes that an International Code may eventually result. There is a large measure of agreement between recent codes but differences do exist between codes and also between what is laid down in the codes and what is actually done. I have not, therefore, followed any one code rigidly although I have referred to some of them.

I am grateful to Dr J. H. Callomon, Dr W. T. Dean, Prof. I. Hessland, Mr M. Mitchell and Dr G. A. Oldershaw for reading parts of the book and suggesting improvements. Mr R. Dean has drawn most of the figures, Mr B. Nettleton has done photographic work in connection with the illustrations, and Mrs E. Walker has typed the text.

I acknowledge, with thanks, permission to reproduce or adapt illustrations from the following: Prof. O. M. B. Bulman; Dr J. H. Callomon; Dr G. Henningsmoen; Prof. I. Hessland; Dr B. F. Howell; Dr P. B. King; Dr J. A. McGowan; Dr R. C. Moore; and Dr C. Teichert; The American Association of Petroleum Geologists; Messrs Birkhäuser; British Railways Board (Historical Records Office); The Bureau of Economic Geology, Texas; the Geological Society of London; the Geological Society of America; the Geological Survey of Great Britain; the Hydrographer of the Navy; the Illinois State Geological Survey; Messrs Oliver & Boyd; the Service de la Carte géologique d'Alsace et de Lorraine; the Systematics Association; the University of Stockholm; and Messrs John Wiley.

D. T. D.

9th December, 1965

CONTENTS

ESTABLISHING
THE SUCCESSION

STRATIGRAPHY is the study of the stratified or sedimentary rocks: their nature, arrangement, and correlation from place to place. It enables geological events, as recorded in the rocks, to be placed in their correct sequence and is thus the key to the history of the earth's crust. Stratification, or arrangement in layers, had been observed by a number of geological pioneers in the eighteenth century, and several of these, notably John Strachey in England (1719) and J. G. Lehmann in Germany (1756), made the further observation that layers of different kinds occurred in the same order within a particular area. With the realization that the sedimentary rocks were laid down layer by layer, it was clear that the upper layers, in an undisturbed section, must be younger than the lower: the principle of *superposition*. From a sequence of rocks could be inferred a sequence of events. This was the theoretical approach developed by James Hutton (1726–1797) who laid the philosophical foundations of modern geology in his famous work, *Theory of the Earth* (1788: 1795). Hutton showed that the rocks recorded events which had occupied an immensely long period of time and established many of the principles by which this record could be interpreted. He saw that there had been periods of upheaval separated by times of denudation and of sedimentation, and that these had alternated not once but many times— his 'succession of former worlds'. He appreciated the significance of unconformities as proving this succession. He lacked only one thing: the means of correlating or identifying his succession of worlds in different parts of the globe. He could recognize the Old Red Sandstone in different parts of Scotland by its characteristic rock-types, but was unable to recognize rocks of the same age in different facies. Thus, although Hutton established the principles of relative dating, he was unable to put them into practice to establish a general history of the earth's crust.

The deficiency was made good by William Smith (1769–1839). Smith discovered the principles of stratigraphy independently while surveying and building the Somerset Coal Canal southwest of Bath from 1793 onwards. As well as understanding stratification and superposition, he began to collect fossils, and by about 1795 had made the discovery for which he is famous, that each group of rocks, or stratum (in modern usage a formation), is characterized by its own distinctive set of fossils. Smith used the principle to trace strata over comparatively short distances. Soon it was extended to correlate strata of the same age which were formed of dissimilar kinds of rock, often over long distances. This is discussed further in Chapter 2.

Smith's criteria for defining a stratum were, then, twofold: a distinctive series of rocks, containing (in most cases) a distinctive fauna. When, in 1799, Smith dictated his first table of strata he was able to list no less than twenty-three distinct strata from the Coal to the Chalk. The original written copy of this document, preserved by the Geological Society of London, is almost illegible. An early printed copy is reproduced opposite. It is a model stratigraphical table, with lithology, thickness, characteristic fossils and typical localities for many of the strata. We can learn an interesting lesson by comparing it with the modern version of the table for southern England. Certain parts of it are very detailed: the strata numbered 8, 9 and 10, are all part of what is now called Upper Fuller's Earth, which is not subdivided today because it is seldom exposed. No doubt the beds were familiar to Smith in excavations. Similarly strata 4, 5 and 6 are now included in undivided Forest Marble. By contrast other prominent formations are absent altogether. Throughout much of its outcrop the predominantly marly and clayey Lias (no. 14) is divided by a highly fossiliferous limestone, the Marlstone, which forms a conspicuous feature in the landscape. Unfortunately for Smith, the Marlstone is absent around Bath, and was therefore omitted from his earlier tables of strata. He first noted it in his published work in 1817. Several Upper Jurassic and Lower Cretaceous strata, which occur between nos. 3 (Oxford Clay), and 2 (Upper Greensand),

Order of the Strata and their imbedded Organic Remains, in the Vicinity of Bath; examined and proved prior to 1799,

BY WILLIAM SMITH, ENGINEER AND MINERAL SURVEYOR.

Strata.	Thickness	Springs.	Fossils, Petrifactions, &c. &c.	Descriptive Characters and Situations.
1 Chalk	300	Intermitting on the Downs	Echinites, Pyrites, Mytilites, Dentalia, funnel-shaped Corals, and Madrepores, Nautilites, Strombites, Cochlæ, Ostreæ, Serpulæ.	Strata of Silex, imbedded.
2 Sand	70	Between the Black Dog and Berkley.		The fertile Vales intersecting Salisbury Plain and the Downs.
3 Clay	30			
4 Sand and Stone	30	Hinton, Norton, Woolverton, Bradford Leigh.		Imbedded is a thin Stratum of calcareous Grit. The Stones flat, smooth, and rounded at the Edges.
5 Clay	15			
6 Forest Marble	10		A Mass of Anomiæ and high-waved Cockles, with calcareous Cement.	The Cover of the upper Bed of Freestone, or Oolyte.
7 Freestone	60		Scarcely any Fossils besides the Coral	Oolyte. resting on a thin Bed of Coral.—Prior Park. Southstoke, Twinny, Winsley, Farley Castle, Westwood, Berfield, Conkwell, Monkton Farley, Coldhorn, Marshfield, Coldashton.
8 Blue Clay	6	Above Bath.		Visible at a Distance, by the Slips on the Declivities of the Hills round Bath.
9 Yellow Clay	8			
10 Fuller's Earth.	6			
11 Bastard ditto, and Sundries	80		Striated Cardia, Mytilites, Anomia, Pundibs, and Duckmuscles.	
12 Freestone	80		Top-covering Anomiæ with calcareous Cement, Strombites, Ammonites Nautilites, Cochlæ Hippocephaloides, fibrous Shell resembling Amianth, Cardia, prickly Cockle Mytilitea, lower Stratum of Coral, large Scollop, Nidus of the Muscle with its Cables	Lincombe. Devonshire Buildings. Englishcombe, Englishbatch, Wilmerton, Dunkerton, Coombay, Munkton Coombe, Wellow, Mitford, Stoke. Freshford, Claverton, Bathford, Beaston, and Hampton, Charlcombe, Swainswick, Tadwick, Langridge.
13 Sand	30		Ammonites, Belemnites	Sand Burs.
14 Marl Blue	40	Round Bath	Pectenites, Belemnites, Gryphites, high-waved Cockles	Ochre Balls.—Mineral Springs of Lincombe, Middle-Hill, Cheltenham.
15 Lias Blue	25		Same as the Marl with Nautilites, Ammonites, Dentalia, and Fragments of the Enchrinni	The fertile Marl Lands of Somersetshire. Twerton, Newton, Preston, Clutton, Stanton Prior, Timsbury, Palton, Marksbury, Farmborough, Corston, Hunstreet, Burnet, Keynsham, Whitchurch, Salford, Kelston, Weston, Pucklechurch, Queencharlton, Norton-malreward, Knowle, Charlton. Kilmersdon, Babington.
16 Ditto White	15			

Fig. 1. Part of William Smith's first table of strata. From a copy in the Historical Records Office, British Railways Board.

WILLIAM SMITH'S STRATA AND THEIR MODERN EQUIVALENTS

Present-day subdivisions	Smith's map, 1815	Smith's table, 1799
London Clay	London Clay	—
Woolwich and Reading Beds, etc. (also East Anglian Crags)	Clay and brickearth / Sand and light loam	—
Chalk	Chalk	1. Chalk
Upper Greensand	Green Sand, parallel to the Chalk	2. Sand
Gault	—	
Lower Greensand	—	
Wealden Beds	—	
Purbeck Beds	—	
Portland Beds	—	
Kimmeridge Clay	Blue Marl, or Oaktree Soil	
Corallian Beds (also other formations)	Purbeck Stone, Kentish Rag, and Limestone of the Vale of Pickering	
Lower Greensand, etc.	Iron Sand or Carstone	3. Clay
Oxford Clay	Clunch Clay or Shale	
Cornbrash	Cornbrash Limestone	4. Sand and Stone
		5. Clay
Forest Marble	Forest Marble and Clay	6. Forest Marble
		7. Freestone
		8. Blue Clay
Great Oolite / Fuller's Earth	Great Oolyte or Bath Freestone	9. Yellow Clay
		10. Fuller's Earth
		11. Bastard ditto and sundries

Inferior Oolite	Under Oolyte	{ 12. Freestone
Midford Sand		13. Sand
Upper Lias Clay	Blue Marl Pastures	14. Marl Blue
Marlstone		
Lower Lias Clay	Blue and White Lias Limestones	{ 15. Lias Blue
Blue Lias		16. Ditto White
White Lias		17. Blue Marl
Rhaetic Beds	Red Marl, Millstone and Breciated Limestone	{ 18. Red-ground
Keuper Marl		19. Millstone
Bunter Sandstone		
Magnesian Limestone	Magnesian Limestone	—
Coal Measures	Coal Measures	{ 20. Pennant Stone
		21. Grays
		22. Cliff
		23. Coal
Carboniferous Limestone	Derbyshire Limestone	—
Old Red Sandstone	Red and Dunstone	—
(Various Palaeozoic formations)	Hardstone, Limestone and Slate	—
Upper Palaeozoic slates of S.W. England	Killas and Slate	
(Various igneous and metamorphic rocks)	Granite, Sienite and Gneiss	—

were likewise omitted because they have been removed by
pre-Upper Greensand erosion from the country between Bath
and Warminster (Wilts.) where Smith evidently first studied the
upper part of his succession (fig. 2, line A-A). If he had gone
only a few miles to the north-east (line B-B) he would have seen
three more formations, the Corallian Beds, Kimmeridge Clay
and Portland Beds, although for the full sequence in the
Upper Jurassic and Lower Cretaceous he would have had to
go to the south coast and the Weald.

Thus we see that a local succession is liable to be incomplete.
To establish the full sequence in an area, one must compare
and combine a number of local successions. The method was
described by Lyell in his *Elements of Geology* (1838, p. 278):

'In order, therefore, to establish a chronological succession of
fossiliferous groups, a geologist must begin with a single section,
in which several sets of strata lie one upon the other. He must
then trace these formations, by attention to their mineral
character and fossils, continuously, as far as possible, from the
starting point. As often as he meets with new groups, he must
ascertain by superposition their age relatively to those first
examined, and thus learn how to intercalate them in a tabular
arrangement of the whole.'

The sequence recorded by Smith was not based on direct
observation, but on inference. Only a small part of it is actually
exposed around Bath In 1793, while levelling along the line of
the proposed canal, Smith had discovered that strata which
occurred on the hilltops at the western end of his line lay in
the valley at the eastern end; in other words, there was an
easterly dip. By making the assumption that this dip was general
throughout the area, beyond the valleys in which it had been
proved by levelling, it was clear that the strata lying further to
the east must be the higher, even if sections showing their actual
order of superposition were not seen. Thus the Chalk, the
easternmost stratum known to Smith at the time, must be the
highest. The assumption proved to be justified and the inference
correct. It was confirmed by mapping, for by tracing his strata
across country Smith found the extension of their outcrops,
the strike, to lie roughly north and south, at right angles to
the dip. This indirect method of establishing the succession by

mapping is, in fact, the usual one in areas where extensive exposures are uncommon.

Where exposed sections are lacking and the order of super-position cannot be established by mapping because of complex tectonics, other criteria may have to be found. If formations are fossiliferous and the faunal sequence is well known from other areas, the succession may be established beyond doubt even though it cannot be observed directly or mapped. Thus in many parts of the world there is little difficulty in deciding upon the relative ages of fossiliferous formations. If fossils are absent difficulties are much greater. Radiometric dating, discussed in Chapter 4, can be used where a series of sediments contains intrusive or interbedded igneous rocks which can be dated, or glauconitic rocks which can be dated by the potassium-argon method.

The phenomenon of *contained fragments* is sometimes useful. If a formation contains pieces of another formation it must be younger than that formation. The method may be applied both to large fragments and, by microscopical study, to the constituent grains of medium and fine grained clastic rocks. It has many limitations, the chief being the difficulty of finding fragments whose source is beyond doubt. It is thus most successful when the fragments are of complex and unusual rock types, most uncertain when they are mineral grains. Contained fragments have figured largely in the attempts to work out the geological succession in the Pre-Cambrian rocks of the Welsh Borderland, and prove that the sedimentary Long-myndian is younger than the highly distinctive Uriconian volcanics, of which it contains pebbles.

In regions of complex tectonics sedimentary sequences may be turned upside down. In piecing together a succession one must know whether beds at individual exposures are the right way up or not. This may be determined in various ways, reviewed in detail by R. R. Shrock (1948).

Improvements to our knowledge of the stratigraphy of well-known areas are coming to depend more and more upon boreholes, as witness the extensive programme of drilling undertaken for research purposes by the British Geological Survey since the war. In areas being studied for economic reasons exploration often includes boreholes at an early stage.

B

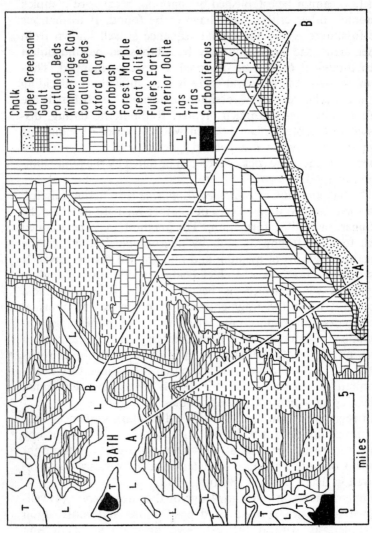

FIG. 2. Geological map of the area south and east of Bath. Based on Crown Copyright Geological Survey map by permission of the Controller of H.M. Stationery Office.

Chalk
Upper Greensand
Gault
Portland Beds
Kimmeridge Clay
Corallian Beds
Oxford Clay
Cornbrash
Forest Marble
Great Oolite
Fuller's Earth
Inferior Oolite
Lias
Trias
Carboniferous

BATH

miles

0   5

Borehole logging is thus a desirable part of the practical stratigrapher's experience, and if the hole is cored the core must be searched as thoroughly as possible for fossils. In addition to providing a complete succession which is rarely obtained from natural exposures, boreholes allow specialized methods of logging, mentioned further in Chapter 3.

I have mentioned that William Smith's first table of strata was inconsistent in degree of subdivision, containing some large subdivisions (e.g. Chalk) and some very small ones, for example those within the Fuller's Earth. In his published works and in his maps Smith did not use these very small units, for by then experience had no doubt taught him that the smallest subdivisions could not be traced very far. Instead he adopted a set of units of more nearly equal size, each distinguished by a particular name. Thus originated the concept of a fundamental unit in stratigraphy, which could be easily distinguished from the units above and below and could be traced across the country by means of its distinctive lithology and fossils. Smith called this unit a stratum. Today it is known in the English-speaking world as a *formation*. This category of unit has become known in recent years as a *rock-stratigraphical* or *lithostratigraphical* unit, to distinguish it from units defined solely by fossils, known as *biostratigraphical* units, which are discussed in Chapter 2. There is a fundamental difference between the two. Rock-stratigraphical units are bounded by changes in lithology which may vary in age from place to place. Biostratigraphical units have boundaries which often approximate to surfaces of uniform age.

Smith's first comprehensive table of strata to be published accompanied his great map of England and Wales in 1815, and the units which he then adopted (see table, pp. 14, 15) were chosen because they could be mapped over areas of some size. The same criterion of mappability persists 145 years later in the definition of a formation in the American Code of Stratigraphic Nomenclature (American Commission 1961, p. 650). The Code states that the definition of a new formation should be based on mappability on large scales and not solely on a type section, however well-exposed this may be. Type sections are considered below.

The aim of the earliest stratigraphers was to establish the

order of the strata. They were not concerned with the detailed succession within each stratum. Formations consisting of a variety of rock types, or of two or three types in alternating layers, lend themselves easily to further subdivision. An example is the Lower Lias of England. Part of this formation consists of shales and marls in rhythmic alternation, studied by W. D. Lang (1924) on the south coast. A small part of his tabulated section follows:

49   5 in. Grey Ledge. B.100. W.4 (partim). S.54. Impersistent limestone of varying thickness up to about 5 inches. *Ammonites* (*sensu stricto*) ? sp.; 5141, *Avicula* sp. *Plagiostoma* sp. *Liogryphaea* sp. *Belemnites* sp. Lignite. '*C. bucklandi*' recorded in Survey Memoir.

48   7 in. Grey Ledge Shales. B.99. W.4 (partim). S.53. *Arnioceras* ? sp.; 5685. *Pecten* sp.; 5266. *Lima acuticostata* Münster; 5267. *Astarte* sp.; 5268. And at the base:—*Paracoroniceras* aff. *gmuendense* (Oppel). *P.* aff. *crossi* (Wright). *Arnioceras* aff. *geometricus* (Oppel). *A. ceratitoides* (Quenstedt). *Ammonites* spp.; all colld. by L. F. Spath.

47   10 in. Glass Bottle. B.98. W.5. S.52. Strong persistent limestone. *Paracoroniceras* ? sp.; 5142. 'Large *C. bucklandi* on under surface' recorded in Survey Memoir.

46   2 ft. 7 in. Glass Bottle shales. B.97. W.6. S.51. *Charmasseiceras* sp.; 5143, 5147–8. *Arnioceras* ? sp.; 5138–40. Urchin spines; 5150. *Inoceramus* sp.; 5144–6. *Pecten* (*Chlamys*) sp. cf. *P. calvus* Goldfuss; 5149.

   46g.   6 in. Conchoidal marl.
   46f.   6 in. Paper shale.
   46e.   2 in. Conchoidal marl. *Arnioceras* ? sp.; 5675–84.
   46d.   2 in. Paper shale.
   46c.   6 in. Conchoidal marl. *Arnioceras* ? sp.; 5669–74.
   46b.   5 in. Paper shale.
   46a.   4 in. Conchoidal marl.

45   9 in. Top Quick. B.96. W.7. S.50. Limestone. '*C. bucklandi*' and saurian remains recorded in Survey Memoir.

44   1 ft. 5 in. Top Quick shales. B.95. W.8. S.49. *Charmasseiceras* spp.; 5661–5.

The purpose of such an exercise is often to record the distribution of the fossils as precisely as possible. For Smith, each stratum had its characteristic fossils. We now know that some fossils may be restricted to a small part of the thickness of a stratum, while others range beyond it. From a detailed succession such as that given above, the vertical ranges of the fossils may be found, and those which are zonally useful distinguished from those which have long ranges.

In formations of uniform lithology other methods have to be adopted. Arthur Vaughan (1905) made a zonal study of the Carboniferous Limestone, starting with the section in the gorge of the Avon at Bristol which exposes nearly the whole 2,300 feet of the Limestone. The limestone had been divided into lithological units but Vaughan did not use these subdivisions, and did not give a detailed lithological section with fossils recorded bed by bed. His subdivision was into biostratigraphical units: zones and subzones. The fauna of each zone and subzone was summarized, and range-diagrams given for corals and brachiopods. This zonal scheme is reviewed on page 41.

Vaughan and others studied many other outcrops of Carboniferous Limestone, but the Avon Gorge provides the most complete section and formed the basis of the zonal scheme. It is regarded as the *type section* for Vaughan's scheme of zoning.

A type section is a standard which may be referred to when identifying a stratigraphical unit elsewhere, or re-studied when a better definition of it is needed. In areas which have been geologically explored in recent times type sections have sometimes been deliberately defined. In the classic geological areas of north-west Europe they have often become fixed by usage rather than by conscious designation. It has generally been assumed that a formation or other unit named after a locality has its type section at that place. Support for this assumption is found in the work of early geologists who, while they did not always specify type-sections, were careful in selecting localities after which they named formations. Thus R. I. Murchison writing in 1839 says: 'The Wenlock Limestone is in every respect identical with the well-known rock of Dudley, and contains the same organic remains. Here, however, it exhibits relations to the superior and inferior strata which do not exist at Dudley, and hence the name of "Wenlock" has been preferred.' And again,

'At Dudley . . . no evidence whatever can be obtained to prove its place in the geological Series; in Shropshire, on the contrary, a clear order of superposition exhibits all the . . . relations required . . . Whilst, therefore, the type of the formation . . . is derived from examples in Shropshire, any peculiarities in these rocks at Dudley and other places will be mentioned in separate and subsequent descriptions.'

By a curious coincidence, James Hall in North America in the same year wrote:

'It thus becomes a desideratum to distinguish rocks by names which cannot be traduced, and which . . . will never prove fallacious. The basis of this nomenclature is derived from localities; and the rock or group will receive its name from the place where it is best developed. For example, the rock denominated in the section calcareous shale . . . will be called Rochester shale. In lithological characters it is extremely like one far higher in the series, but the fossil contents are entirely different . . . the characters if studied and well understood at Rochester will guide the observer in all subsequent determinations' (quoted by Schuchert 1943).

Nearly 120 years later, C. O. Dunbar and J. Rodgers (1957) echoed Murchison and Hall: 'The [type] section should, if possible, be completely exposed, and at any rate, it should show the top and base of the formation . . . It is very desirable also that the section should be fossiliferous . . . and that at least preliminary faunal lists accompany the original description.'

In the case of highly variable formations, the type section should ideally show a thick and, as far as possible, complete development. In practice the choice will be limited by sections available. Many stratigraphical units have more or less unsuitable type localities. The English Oxford Clay is poorly exposed at Oxford, and could certainly not be adequately defined from permanent sections there. William Buckland, who named it in 1818, was an Oxford professor. The French palaeontologist A. d'Orbigny named a number of units after places which he had never seen; consequently the visitor to Kellaways (Wiltshire, England), type locality of the Callovian Stage, will see green fields with one or two riverbank exposures showing only a small part of the stage. Type localities will be discussed further in Chapter 8.

Type localities do not have any 'official' or internationally agreed status like type specimens have in the biological sciences. On the whole, there seems little need for them to have such formal recognition. Stratigraphers manage well enough as things are, and any increase in clarity which might result from more rigid rules would probably be offset by time spent on 'legal' arguments as to the eligibility and priority of type sections.

The thicker a stratigraphical unit is, the more unlikely is it that a single section or area will be a satisfactory standard of reference. When we come to units as large as systems, the type section or type region concept almost disappears. No one today would attempt to use Devon, England, as type region for the Devonian System, nor the Jura Mountains for the Jurassic. Nor is anyone inconvenienced because units not named after places, such as the Cretaceous or the Old Red Sandstone, have no predetermined type localities.

In many cases a local succession falls naturally into lithological units: Smith's succession at Bath is an example. The Inferior Oolite (no. 12 of Smith's original table) is clearly defined by abrupt changes of rock-type from sand below and to clay above. Difficulties occur in fixing boundaries where there is a gradual change of rock type from one formation to another. This is the case with the Kimmeridge Clay (below) and Portland Sand (above) on the coast of Dorset, England (Fig. 3). At least three different levels have been adopted for the boundary by different workers. After two attempts to fix a line corresponding to the actual transition from clay to sand, in 1888–90 the Geological Survey adopted a third and lower line at the base of a six-foot sandstone, the Massive Bed, although the marls above this bed are indistinguishable from those below. The line is the only one which can be easily traced throughout the area. In cases of gradual change boundaries must, then, be arbitrary, and will usually be chosen on grounds of expediency.

A further difficulty occurs where the lithology of a formation changes as it is traced along the outcrop. The change is gradual so that the place where one formation gives place to the other must be arbitrarily decided or left indefinite. Natural circumstances may decide for us: the Gault clay (Albian) of south-eastern England is replaced further north, in Norfolk and Lincolnshire, by the Red Chalk, but the transition is concealed by the Recent deposits of the Fens.

Zoning by fossils often shows that the lower and upper

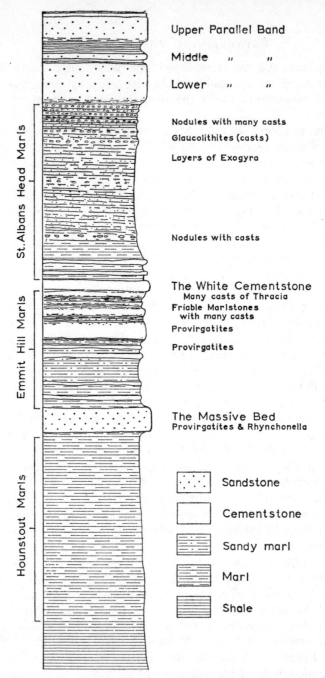

FIG. 3. Section through the uppermost Kimmeridge Clay and part of the Portland Sand near St. Alban's Head, Dorset, England, to show lithological transition and alternation. After Arkell (1947), by permission of the Controller of H.M. Stationery Office.

limits of a formation are not everywhere of the same age. This phenomenon will be discussed further in Chapter 5. I will point out here that such variation is not a reason for changing the name, provided that the distinctive lithology of the formation persists. The formation is a mass of rock; there are other concepts (zones, stages) in terms of which changes in age may be expressed. This has not always been understood. In southern England, the sands between the Upper Lias clays and the Inferior Oolite limestones have been locally named (from south to north) Bridport Sands, Yeovil Sands and Midford Sands, and these names were accepted by S. S. Buckman as usefully expressing the gradual change in age of the sands (they get older as they are traced northwards). The need for these terms is questionable, and they cannot be geographically demarcated from one another. So long as it is accepted that few formations have constant age limits the need for such expedients vanishes.

Formations may be formally subdivided, the subdivisions being often recognizable over a more limited area than the formation as a whole. It is easier to know what to regard as a formation in North America than in Britain, for in North America the word 'formation' is commonly part of the name, although in earlier US practice the locality name was often combined with a rock name; thus Rochester Shale, Burgess Shale, Beekmantown Limestone. In Britain stratigraphical nomenclature has been less consciously formulated than in North America, and the name is usually locality + rock type (Harlech Grits, Oxford Clay), locality + 'beds' (Bracklesham Beds), or else some descriptive or vernacular term (Red Crag, Gault). There are disadvantages in the British practice, which is both inconsistent and misleading, but it is too late to change it now. It is inconsistent because the rank of a unit in the classification is not obvious: the uninitiated might suppose that Hastings Beds and Wealden Beds in the Lower Cretaceous have the same status, but in fact the former is a subdivision of the latter. It is misleading when formations have been named from some conspicuous but minor component: the Millstone Grit, in the Carboniferous of the Pennines, contains more shale than grit. British stratigraphers are used to these anomalies, but they are probably infuriating to others.

In North America subdivisions of formations are known as members, if persistent, or tongues or lentils if impersistent. In Britain these terms are not used and there is no regular scale of nomenclature.

In North America the category above the formation is the *group* and this term is recommended for general use by the Stratigraphic Subcommission of the International Geological Congress. In Britain, the term *series* has been used in some parts of the stratigraphical column, but has found little favour in others. Again there is no uniform practice. Some units have changed status with increased knowledge. Originally the Millstone Grit and Inferior Oolite, of the British Carboniferous and Jurassic respectively, were regarded as single formations; each is now subdivided and would generally be regarded as a series or group comprising a number of formations. The term series is also widely used as a biostratigraphical unit and is discussed further on pages 148, 150.

The local succession is thus the foundation of all stratigraphy. Except where there are good natural sections this is usually worked out by mapping, and it may be extended by tracing lithological formations through into areas where a higher or lower part of the succession can be studied. The sequence thus built up will be a sequence of formations. To provide a stratigraphical framework valid over a larger area, the succession of fossils must be worked out and a scheme of stages or zones set up which can be traced independently of local lithology. This process will be described in the next chapter.

2

CORRELATION
BY FOSSILS

THE local succession is the foundation of stratigraphy, but for many geological purposes we must compare and synthesize a number of local successions, whether to build up a more extensive succession or to assemble evidence as to past conditions over a wider area. For either purpose we need to identify rocks of the same age in different places. This is the process of correlation and, if it progresses beyond the identification of a single instant of time, involves the concept of a time-scale on which various events can be placed in their correct order of occurrence.

The passage of time may be measured in two ways: by observing some process which is unidirectional and non-reversible, or by observing the number of repetitions of some event which occurs at regular intervals. The first is exemplified by the burning down of a candle, and candles have in fact been used as clocks; the second by the rotation of the earth or the swing of a pendulum. There is an important difference between the two methods: in the first, the point to which the candle has burnt down provides a simple and unambiguous measure of the time which has passed since it was lit. In the second, we must count the number of repetitions by using a calendar or a clock mechanism. Both methods are used to measure the passage of geological time, but the first is more important than the second.

Only two kinds of unidirectional, non-reversible process are of general use at present to the geologist: radioactive decay and the evolution of living organisms. Radioactive decay can provide an age in terms of fixed units such as years, and is the only method available for Pre-Cambrian or Cryptozoic rocks, and for direct dating of igneous and metamorphic rocks of any age. In the fossiliferous rocks radiometric dating has so far been of minor importance, partly because it was developed much later than the other method, partly because many sediments lack syngenetic minerals which can at present be dated radiometrically. In its present stage of development it provides a much less sensitive means of subdividing rocks than zoning by fossils.

The progress of organic evolution can be used because at every instant the fauna and flora of the world is unique, different from all past and all future assemblages. By collecting from known successions we can establish the sequence of assemblages, or rather of those members which are found fossil, and we can then place newly discovered assemblages in the scale, either by direct comparison or by interpolation. Since rates of evolution are highly variable, and cannot in general be determined, we cannot use units of defined length with this method; we can only place events in sequence, and our smallest units will depend in practice on the smallest amount of evolutionary change which can be detected.

Recurrent events have been little used on account of the difficulty in counting the number of repetitions. In a few cases, such as varved sediments, the recurrent events can be recognized as years. In others, such as cyclic sedimentation, or the climatic cycles of the Pleistocene, they are of unknown and variable duration. Methods dependent on these phenomena can at best be used for short sections of geological time, and their position in the sequence must be found by radiometric or palaeontological methods.

Units of subdivision defined by fossils have become known as *biostratigraphical* units, the understanding being that they approximate to subdivisions whose boundaries are everywhere of the same age, or *isochronous*. The reasons for supposing this will be discussed later in this chapter. Radiometric dating and other methods of correlation will occupy later chapters.

Smith's discovery that each formation is characterized by distinctive fossils was an empirical one. Moreover, stated in this form, it is of limited usefulness. It was soon realized, however, that fossils could be used as indicators of age irrespective of the rock-type in which they were found. An early example of their use in this way was Charles Lyell's subdivision of the Tertiary. Together with the French palaeontologist G. P. Deshayes he made an extensive study of the Tertiary rocks of western Europe. They found that mollusc species still living also occurred as fossils, but that the older the rocks, the smaller the number of Recent (i.e. living) species in the fossil fauna. The older formations had a correspondingly larger number of extinct species. On this basis three subdivisions were proposed, Eocene, Miocene and Pliocene, with increasing proportions of Recent species in each. Lyell's original definitions (1833) were:

Pliocene Period	49% of molluscan species are still living
Miocene Period	18% ,, ,, ,, ,,
Eocene Period	$3\frac{1}{4}$% ,, ,, ,, ,,

In addition to this simple mode of definition it was found that rocks of each period yielded certain characteristic species which were not found in rocks of the other periods. Major changes in Tertiary molluscan faunas were thus demonstrated.

As knowledge of the succession of faunas advanced during the first half of the nineteenth century it became necessary to try to explain it in terms of theories then current. The statement in the first book of Genesis, that living nature had been created at one episode and had thereafter remained unchanged, became inadequate. Georges Cuvier (1769–1832) in 1812 postulated a series of revolutions, each of which destroyed the animal life of a particular area, which was then colonized by a different fauna which had previously existed elsewhere. This explanation, also, was soon recognized as inadequate. Lyell (1832) and H. T. de la Beche (1834) believed that there had been a 'succession of creations as new conditions arose', and d'Orbigny (1802–1857), whose researches had led him to distinguish 27 successive faunas in the fossil record then known, believed that each in turn became extinct and was replaced by the creation of a new fauna of world-wide distribution. On this basis he divided the sedimentary succession into 27 stages. Like Lyell's Tertiary subdivisions each stage was identified by its diagnostic fauna independently of the local lithology. Lyell was the first to subdivide rocks on the basis of their fauna alone and d'Orbigny was the first to provide a complete scheme for the whole fossiliferous succession.

As knowledge grew the number of postulated creations would doubtless have been further increased, but the process was halted by the publication in 1859 of Charles Darwin's *Origin of Species*. The idea of evolution had existed for some time. It was championed in the late eighteenth century by Darwin's grandfather Erasmus, and during the first half of the nineteenth century many naturalists had toyed with it. J. B. de Lamarck in France, Robert Chambers in Scotland and others published theories of evolution, but the evidence which they put forward was not compelling enough to persuade most naturalists to abandon creation especially as influential geologists such as Lyell deliberately rejected evolution. Darwin adduced a mass of evidence in favour of his mechanism of evolution by natural selection, so that it became impossible to ignore evolution and many naturalists soon accepted it.

The basis for correlation under d'Orbigny's scheme was the belief that each fauna was created simultaneously throughout the globe. Darwin's theory removed any such precise basis for correlation, and explained the succession of faunas by evolution. To begin with it was not found easy to recognize cases of evolution among fossils, and Darwin devoted a chapter of his book to explaining the apparent absence from the rocks of a continuous gradation of forms, stressing the incompleteness of the sedimentary record. It was some years before evolutionary sequences of fossils began to be recognized and described. Meanwhile, in 1862, T. H. Huxley (1825–1895) delivered a celebrated address to the Geological Society of London on 'Geological Contemporaneity'. Huxley criticized the supposed precision of stratigraphical correlations, and although he did not mention any names he may have had d'Orbigny's ideas in mind. According to Huxley, all that geology could show was that the order of succession of faunas had been the same in different areas. For this similarity of succession he invented the term *homotaxis*. Two formations, in different areas, which contained the same fauna could be said to be homotaxial: each occupied the same position in the succession of faunas. There was no proof that they were deposited at the same time.

Huxley's address made a strong impression when it was delivered. Nevertheless we can now see it as an essentially retrograde step in the progress of stratigraphy, although the concept of homotaxis has been a useful one. The pre-Darwinian stratigraphy which Huxley was criticizing, although wrong in its philosophical foundation, was essentially right in practice.

According to the theory of evolution, the faunal changes which we observe are due to evolutionary change of some species, and the extinction of others. Rates of evolution vary greatly. A few forms have remained almost unchanged for long periods of geological time—the brachiopod *Lingula* and the bivalve mollusc *Nucula* are classic examples. Most animals evolved faster than this. D'Orbigny found that it was exceptional for a species to range through more than one stage, and later work has shown that some are confined to a small part of a stage. To obtain precision in correlation, therefore, we should use organisms which show rapid evolutionary change. Before elaborating on this point, however, we must consider the question which worried Huxley and many others: were faunal changes simultaneous throughout the world?

The factor which caused concern was the rate of migration. Having originated in one area, how long did it take a species, or a fauna, to spread into other areas? If it took a long time by comparison with the duration of stratigraphical units, then clearly units defined by fossils would not be of the same age in different places. Further, it was supposed that migration might be delayed until conditions in a distant area happened to be congenial to the new forms.

Doubts of this kind have haunted some stratigraphers from Huxley until the present time. When they were first raised there was no reliable knowledge of the length of geological time, of evolutionary processes or rates of migration. With present knowledge the doubts can be resolved. First, we know that a species, which usually consists of a number of local populations covering a more or less wide geographical area, evolves as a whole (p. 58). If we find fossil remains of the same evolutionary lineage in different areas, it is reasonable to assume that they occurred within a continuous geographical range, and that corresponding points on the lineage in different places were contemporaneous. Many of the fossil sequences used in stratigraphy are of this kind. In other cases, where a new species or fauna suddenly appears in a succession, there has clearly been migration. Present knowledge indicates that migration or dispersal, even of species which are sessile in the adult, is rapid in terms of geological time, within the limits set by physical conditions.

Rapid dispersal seems to be an important factor in survival of the species, and many plants and invertebrate animals have stages in the life history which have been specially evolved to secure this. The physical limits to dispersal, or at least to the survival and reproduction of the dispersed individuals, are important. Their effect in the past has given rise to *facies faunas*, which are restricted to certain environments. Facies faunas are discussed further in Chapter 5. Within these physical limits, observations of present-day animals, both terrestrial and aquatic, has shown that they commonly have rates of dispersal which could result in world-wide distribution within a few thousand years. Now, the mean duration of a Jurassic ammonite zone was about a million years, and most other zones were longer. It is clear that the time needed for wide dispersal is negligible compared with the duration of a zone, and the first appearance of a new species over a wide area can be regarded as simultaneous provided that the effects of facies can be discounted.

The Jurassic of north-west Europe is currently divided into about 60 ammonite zones, as a result of investigation and revision over a period of a century. There is still room for improvement, but by and large the scheme works. Not all the zones are found everywhere, but wherever marine Jurassic rocks outcrop the zones which do occur are found in the same order; in other words, the sequence of faunal changes, by which the zones are defined, is the same everywhere. Now it is conceivable that a single faunal change, especially an extinction, might occur at different times in different places, and also that dispersal may sometimes be delayed by physical factors which are later removed. But it is inconceivable, in view of what we now know of evolution and dispersal, that a long and complex series of faunal changes should occur in the same order at different times in different places; that such series should be homotaxial but not simultaneous. The very complexity of modern zonal schemes thus argues strongly in favour of their constituent zones being of the same age wherever they occur.

There is a further consideration, however: the distribution of a species or a fauna is often limited. This is another way of saying that there were zoological provinces in the past as at present, and many animals were restricted to one or another province. Huxley pointed out this difficulty, but exaggerated its importance: he thought that a Devonian fauna and flora might have existed in Britain at the same time as a Silurian one in North America. The probability of this having occurred is now seen to be so remote as to be absurd. Not only are the general aspects of the fauna and flora of a given period similar in different regions, but there are many close parallels in detailed evolutionary sequences. The existence of faunal provinces does give rise to difficulties in correlation, but chiefly because some groups of zones, or more rarely larger divisions, are restricted to certain regions. The validity of correlation within the region is not in doubt, but correlation with other regions may be less precise. This is not the same as Huxley's view that apparently good correlations might in fact be spurious.

ZONES

As the formation is the unit of lithological classification of rocks, so the unit of palaeontological classification is the zone. Modern usage dates from the German Albert Oppel, who wrote in 1856 'Comparison has often been made between whole groups of beds, but it has not been shown that *each horizon*, identifiable in any place by a number of peculiar and constant species, is to be recognized with the same degree of certainty in distant regions. This task is admittedly a hard one, but it is only by carrying it out that an accurate correlation of a whole system can be assured. It necessarily involves exploring the vertical range of each separate species in the most diverse localities, while ignoring the lithological development of the beds; by this means will be brought into prominence those zones which, through the constant and exclusive occurrence of certain species, mark themselves off from their neighbours [i.e. beds above and below] as distinct horizons. In this way is obtained an ideal profile, of which the component parts of the same age in the various districts are characterized always by the same species.'

Oppel makes it clear that certain species were especially valuable for his refined subdivision, and this is stressed by the fact that he named each of his zones after a fossil species, the *index species*, whereas d'Orbigny had named his stages after places or lithological characters.

c

Oppel provided 33 zones for the Jurassic and traced them throughout France, Germany and England, for each locality indicating the beds which represent the zone in terms of local formations. The number has since been increased to about 60.

Ideally the zonal scheme should be related to the evolution of the fossils used to delimit the zones. In practice this is imperfectly realized. We shall now take some actual examples and examine their palaeontological basis.

Most zonal systems were originally set up by trial and error and by selection of whatever index species seemed to be the most suitable: they had some, if not all, of the characteristics usually specified for a good zonal species: limited vertical range, widespread geographical distribution, and reasonably abundant occurrence. From the first it was seen that, in a given part of the succession, some fossil groups were more suitable than others. Often, though not always, one particular group was the obvious choice. Thus throughout the world we associate Cambrian zoning with trilobites, Ordovician and Silurian with graptolites, marine Devonian and Carboniferous with goniatites, Jurassic with ammonites (Fig. 8). Zonal fossils may be more or less restricted to certain rock types or facies, and so for parts of the geological succession two or more zonal schemes are used. Examples are the marine and continental (Old Red Sandstone) facies of the European Devonian, zoned on goniatites and chordates ('fish') respectively. For the Upper Carboniferous no less than three schemes exist side by side, based on goniatites, non-marine lamellibranchs and plants. In these cases detailed correlation may be possible within one zonal system but link-up with a contemporaneous system in rocks of different facies may be difficult, and only to be achieved in broad terms.

ZONES OF THE CHALK

The chalk facies of the Upper Cretaceous was zoned in France by E. Hébert in 1864–1866 and his scheme, as modified by later workers, and adopted in Britain. (*See opposite page*).

The two *Micraster* species, and possibly the *Belemnitella* species, form parts of evolutionary sequences, although this was not known when the zones were set up. The other index fossils are unrelated, arbitrarily chosen because they are abundant or characteristic at particular levels. The zones are recognized, however, not merely by their index species but by the accompanying fauna. They are of the kind known as *assemblage zones* (p. 56). The constituent species of the zonal fauna are them-

ZONES OF THE SOUTHERN ENGLISH CHALK

Belemnitella lanceolata	
Belemnitella mucronata	belemnites
Gonioteuthis [Actinocamax] quadrata	
Offaster pillula	echinoid
Marsupites testudinarius	
Uintacrinus westfalicus	crinoids
Micraster coranguinum	
Micraster cortestudinarium	echinoids
Holaster planus	
Terebratulina lata	brachiopod
Inoceramus labiatus	lamellibranch
Holaster subglobosus	echinoid
Schloenbachia varians	ammonite

selves members of lineages which are evolving at different rates, so one would expect the zonal boundaries to be ill-defined, not all the characteristic species making their appearance at the same horizon. In fact some of the boundaries are sharp due to breaks in sedimentation, and to migration of new forms into the British area.

THE ORDOVICIAN GRAPTOLITE ZONES OF BRITAIN

The graptolite zones of the British Ordovician and Silurian are among the most famous examples of zonal subdivision. The system used in the Ordovician originated in a paper by Charles Lapworth on the Moffat Series in the Southern Uplands of Scotland, published in 1878. The Moffat Series, now abandoned as a stratigraphical unit, included beds now placed in the higher part of the Ordovician and the lowest Silurian. Lapworth divided the Series into three formations. The two upper formations were each subdivided, all the subdivisions except one being fossil zones. (*See page 36*).

Each zone was defined in lithological terms as part of the local succession, as well as by its fossil contents. The zones were used as local subdivisions only and not for general correlation,

though Lapworth showed, by comparing the graptolite successions at Moffat and elsewhere, that (for instance) 'the Moffat
Rocks are the greatly attenuated representatives of enormous
thicknesses of the Welsh Silurians, in which their fossils will be
found to have a vastly extended range'.

LAPWORTH'S SUBDIVISIONS OF THE MOFFAT SERIES

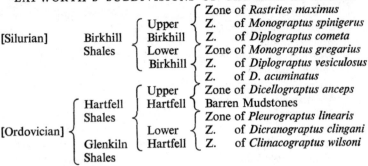

[Silurian]	Birkhill Shales	Upper Birkhill	Zone of *Rastrites maximus*
			Z. of *Monograptus spinigerus*
			Z. of *Diplograptus cometa*
		Lower Birkhill	Zone of *Monograptus gregarius*
			Z. of *Diplograptus vesiculosus*
			Z. of *D. acuminatus*
[Ordovician]	Hartfell Shales	Upper Hartfell	Zone of *Dicellograptus anceps*
			Barren Mudstones
			Zone of *Pleurograptus linearis*
		Lower Hartfell	Z. of *Dicranograptus clingani*
	Glenkiln Shales		Z. of *Climacograptus wilsoni*

The Glenkiln Shales contain fossils but were not given a
zonal name. Two years later, however, Lapworth recognized
the zone of *Coenograptus* (now *Nemagraptus*) *gracilis*, one of
the Glenkiln species, below the *C. wilsoni* Zone, and set up the
Zone of *Dicellograptus complanatus* for the gap represented by
the Barren Mudstones. Lapworth's paper of 1879–1880,
entitled 'On the geological distribution of the Rhabdophora'
was a landmark, for it finally established the stratigraphical
value of the graptolites. In it Lapworth was also able to add
two more zones, for the part of the succession below that known
at Moffat, as a result of studies in England and Wales. Finally,
G. L. Elles in 1904 and Elles and Wood (1906 and 1913) set up
four more zones. The resulting table for the British Ordovician
is on the page opposite.

A number of other zones have been proposed from time to
time, but those listed above have survived the test of actual use
for correlation within the British Isles and to some extent in
neighbouring countries. The zonal table now accepted has
been built up gradually as a result of trial and error. Nevertheless it must have a basis in evolution and migrations which
resulted in the succession of faunas which we actually collect,
for which the zonal table is a convenient shorthand; the zones
are largely assemblage-zones. The full story of this evolution

and migration is not yet understood. O. M. B. Bulman (1958, p. 160) says: 'Contrary perhaps to popular belief, many graptolite zones have a restricted geographical distribution, as is only too apparent to those who attempt the correlation of graptolitic successions.' Bulman goes on to say, however, that 'it is possible to define faunal units which are considerably bigger than zones, but which can be applied over wider

ZONE	AUTHOR OF ZONE
Dicellograptus anceps	Lapworth 1878
D. complanatus	Lapworth 1880
Pleurograptus linearis	Lapworth 1878
Dicranograptus clingani	Lapworth 1878
Climacograptus wilsoni	Lapworth 1878
Climacograptus peltifer	Elles & Wood 1906
Nemagraptus gracilis	Lapworth 1880
Glyptograptus teretiusculus	Elles & Wood 1913
Didymograptus murchisoni	Lapworth 1880
D. bifidus	Lapworth 1880
D. hirundo	Elles 1904
D. extensus	Elles 1904

areas . . .'. This agrees with the experience of other palaeontologists in other parts of the geological succession, and may be expressed as a general rule that larger palaeontological subdivisions are valid for a wider geographical area than smaller ones. There are exceptions to this, as to most rules; for example, Nemagraptus gracilis is of almost world-wide occurrence (Fig. 10). In general, however, local zonal schemes have had to be set up for different regions, correlation between the different local schemes being less precise than that within them.

UPPER CAMBRIAN TRILOBITE ZONES OF SCANDINAVIA

The Upper Cambrian of Scandinavia, which consists dominantly of monotonous black shales, has been subdivided in great detail on the basis of trilobites of the family Olenidae. The latest revision by Gunnar Henningsmoen (1957) is a model piece of stratigraphical palaeontology and enables the palaeontological foundations of the zones and subzones to be examined in detail.

The zones may be considered first. The ranges of the index fossils are shown in Figure 4. The Olenus zones correspond to the vertical range of the genus *Olenus*. The base of the Parabolina spinulosa Zone is marked by the appearance of the genera *Parabolina* and *Protopeltura*, which are both believed to have evolved from *Olenus*, but the index species *Par. spinulosa* has

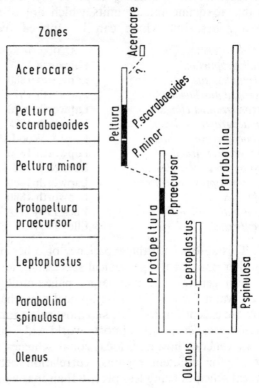

FIG. 4. Ranges of certain genera (open rectangles) and species (black rectangles) of Upper Cambrian trilobites. Broken lines show probable evolutionary connections. From data in Henningsmoen (1957).

been found in the upper part of the zone only, and survived into the lowest part of the next zone. This, the Leptoplastus Zone, is marked by the incoming of the genus *Leptoplastus* which, however, again survived into the succeeding zone. The base of the Protopeltura praecursor Zone is not marked by any conspicuous change in fauna and is, indeed, ill-defined. The zone is marked by species of *Protopeltura* and *Leptoplastus*, and the index species occurs only in the three upper subzones. The division between the Protopeltura praecursor and Peltura minor Zones is marked by the appearance of new species of *Protopeltura* and of other genera, but *Peltura* itself only appears in the upper part of the Peltura minor Zone. The replacement of *P. minor* by *P. scarabaeoides* defines the base of the zone named after the latter species, which does not, however survive to the top of its zone. Finally, the Peltura scarabaeoides–Acerocare Zone boundary is defined on the basis of the succession of species of *Peltura*, and the genus *Acerocare* occurs in the upper part of its zone only, although its probable ancestor *Acerocarina* first appears at or near the base of the zone.

This survey shows that whatever the intentions or beliefs of the founders of the zonal scheme, the ranges of the zonal index species do not define the zones as now recognized. These are defined on the basis of other faunal characters and more particularly in terms of the succession of species in certain genera which allow the zones to be divided into subzones. Examples of these will now be analysed.

Figure 5 shows the evolutionary relationship of certain species of the genus *Ctenopyge*, and in the left-hand column the names of the subzones which have been set up for the Protopeltura and Peltura Zones. *Ctenopyge* has been subdivided into three subgenera. It is at once clear that the subzones of the upper Protopeltura praecursor Zone depend on an evolutionary sequence from *Leptoplastus neglectus* to early species of the subgenus *Eoctenopyge*. The appearance of *Mesoctenopyge* marks the Peltura minor Zone, and again different species of the subgenus characterize subzones, although the third subzonal index, *C. (M) tumida*, is not descended from the index species of the underlying subzone. The emphasis then shifts to the subgenus *Ctenopyge* (*sensu stricto*) and three more subzones are obtained by making use of a line of evolution in the subgenus.

The subzonal scheme is thus seen to be closely related to evolution in the genus *Ctenopyge*. This has two important consequences: first, if successive index species are members of an evolutionary sequence it is unlikely that their ranges will overlap, as may happen if unrelated index species are chosen. The limits of the subzones are exactly defined provided that the species can be defined. Zones corresponding to the total ranges

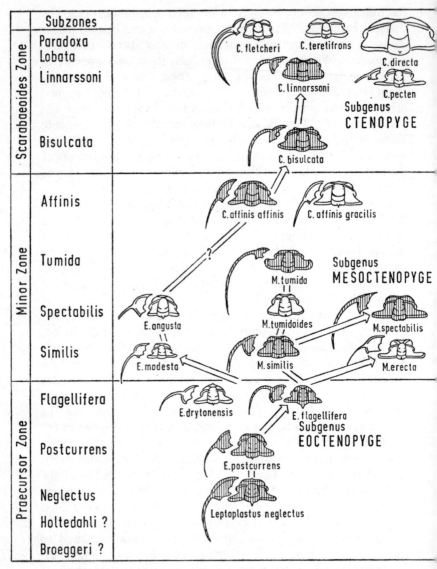

FIG. 5. Diagram showing the relationship of the subzones of the Protopeltura and Peltura Zones of the Upper Cambrian to evolution in the genus *Ctenopyge*. After Henningsmoen (1957). Species used as subzonal indices are shaded. The Lobata and Paradoxa Subzones are not shown in their correct positions relative to the trilobites.

of index species are known as range-zones or biozones (p. 54), and some of the Upper Cambrian subzones are units of this kind. Second, if the same evolutionary sequence is established in different regions, it is likely, from what has been said earlier about evolutionary processes, that corresponding points on the sequence in different places are, for geological purposes, contemporaneous, and good correlation is thus achieved. Henningsmoen believes that the Olenid zonal scheme is valid throughout Scandinavia, Poland, Britain and eastern Canada.

It will be appreciated from Figure 5 that the subzones rest on fine palaeontological distinctions and one would need considerable experience with these fossils before one could be confident of making correct identifications. There have been periodic complaints for nearly a century now that zonal palaeontology was becoming too complicated. It is true that field workers must in many cases be content with comparatively crude palaeontological distinctions, but this is no reason for neglecting detailed subdivision wherever it is possible.

THE CORAL-BRACHIOPOD ZONES OF THE CARBONIFEROUS LIMESTONE OF BRITAIN

A set of zones which has turned out to have been founded on facies fossils was proposed for the Carboniferous Limestone of south-west England by Arthur Vaughan in 1905. After enjoying popularity for many years it later met with some criticism, but is likely to continue in use for correlating the important limestone facies of the British Lower Carboniferous.

The Carboniferous Limestone is a formation or group consisting of a variety of mainly shallow-water, calcareous rock-types and reaching in places a thickness of over 3,000 feet. It is well-exposed and often highly fossiliferous in Somerset, Gloucestershire, South Wales, North Wales, Derbyshire and the North of England. In other areas, including Devon and Cornwall and parts of the north all or a large part of the Lower Carboniferous is in shaly facies which does not yield corals and brachiopods but can be correlated by goniatites.

Vaughan devoted his attention to the corals and brachiopods which are the commonest fossils. He constructed range-diagrams in which he plotted to scale occurrences of various

genera and species in the Carboniferous Limestone of the Avon
Gorge at Bristol which he selected as his type locality. He
attempted to show the total ranges of genera and species and
also the different degrees of abundance in different parts of
each range. On the basis of these range-diagrams Vaughan set
up a system of zones and subzones into which the Carboniferous
Limestone of the Avon Gorge might be divided, and gave some
evidence that the scheme could be applied to other sections
within a radius of about 15 miles of the type section.

Vaughan's original scheme was as follows. The greek letters
denote beds in which the faunas of two contiguous zones
overlap:

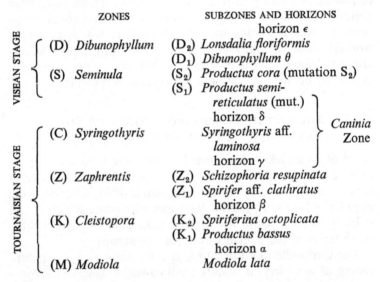

	ZONES	SUBZONES AND HORIZONS
		horizon ε
VISEAN STAGE	(D) *Dibunophyllum*	(D₂) *Lonsdalia floriformis*
		(D₁) *Dibunophyllum θ*
	(S) *Seminula*	(S₂) *Productus cora* (mutation S₂)
		(S₁) *Productus semi-reticulatus* (mut.)
		horizon δ
	(C) *Syringothyris*	*Syringothyris* aff. *laminosa*
		horizon γ
TOURNAISIAN STAGE	(Z) *Zaphrentis*	(Z₂) *Schizophoria resupinata*
		(Z₁) *Spirifer* aff. *clathratus*
		horizon β
	(K) *Cleistopora*	(K₂) *Spiriferina octoplicata*
		(K₁) *Productus bassus*
		horizon α
	(M) *Modiola*	*Modiola lata*

The subzones S_1, *Syringothyris* aff. *laminosa*, and horizons δ and γ are bracketed together as the **Caninia Zone**.

In the introduction to his paper Vaughan gave a clear exposition of the principles which should guide palaeontological
zoning, pointing out (among other things) that '. . . any system
of zonal indices, in which each index is the result . . . of evolution from the one which precedes, has a special value, from the
fact that the relative order is necessarily the same for all
localities'. The importance of this principle has already been
emphasized. Although he stressed the value of this procedure
Vaughan was unable to carry it out in practice. He did not
define his zones by successive members of any one evolutionary

lineage but used arbitrarily chosen index fossils supported by assemblages. A simplified version of his range diagrams, showing only the species used as zonal and subzonal indices, is given in Figure 6. An examination of this shows, first, that none of the zonal index genera or the subzonal index species are closely related to their adjacent index genera or species above or below. Secondly, many of their ranges overlap. A striking example is the brachiopod *Syringothyris* which is abundant from the base of the section up to the top of the zone named after it, with an additional short period of abundance at the top of the succeeding subzone. Now it is true that Vaughan did not intend his zones and subzones to be defined only by their index species; they were defined by assemblages which could be recognized in the absence of the index species. However, the original range diagrams show no species, either coral or brachiopod, restricted to the *Syringothyris* Zone, and there is no species whose first appearance conveniently marks the base of the zone. The palaeontological definition of the zone (it was also defined in terms of lithology at the type section) depends on the common occurrence or abundance, in parts of the zone, of several species which also occur above and below. Furthermore, the beds included in the zone at the type section are poorly fossiliferous and some of the characteristic features were described from other sections which Vaughan correlated with the poorly characterized beds in the Avon section.

Vaughan's work gave an immediate impetus to faunal study of the Lower Carboniferous and the Carboniferous Limestone in other parts of the country was investigated and correlated with the zones in the Avon Gorge. The full succession was traced throughout South Wales but in many parts of central and northern England the limestone facies was found to begin only with the higher zones. Facies other than limestone, for example the Culm facies of West Somerset, Devon and Cornwall, could not be correlated with Vaughan's zones because of the absence of the coral-brachiopod faunas.

At the same time Vaughan and others in the Bristol district made numerous alterations to the zonal scheme in order to accommodate evidence from other sections. Finally, in the opinion of some authors (Welch and Trotter, 1961), by 1915, the year of Vaughan's last paper and of his death, 'the original

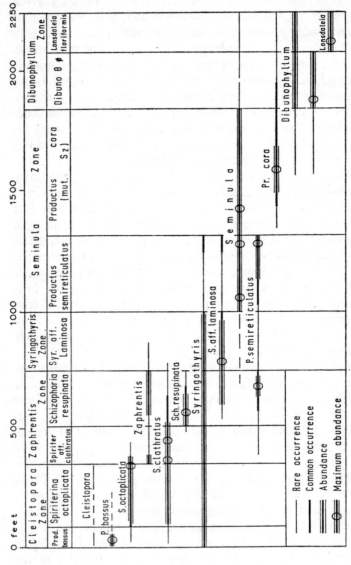

FIG. 6. Ranges of some genera and species of corals and brachiopods in the Carboniferous Limestone of the Avon Gorge, Bristol. After Vaughan (1905).

scheme had become so altered as to be now highly theoretical'. Certainly at this time Vaughan believed that each evolving lineage of species passed through a series of stages ('young stage—adult stage—phylogenetic old age—extinction'), each characterized by a more advanced degree of development of certain characters, and he stated that 'the ideal method of zoning consists in deducing the time [i.e. the stratigraphical horizon] from the stages [of morphological development] at which certain structures have arrived'. This idea that the evolution of a lineage must of necessity follow a certain programme was being applied to Jurassic stratigraphy by S. S. Buckman at about the same time. Detailed study of fossil lineages has shown that this belief is false, and its acceptance for a while was a harmful influence on stratigraphy since the supposed relative ages of two or more fossil horizons was decided according to the supposed evolutionary histories of the fossils, rather than by observation or by correlation with an observed sequence. For example, by such methods Buckman in 1927 recognized no less than eleven brachiopod faunas in the English Cornbrash. Later work showed Buckman's brachiopod succession to be wholly without foundation in fact (Arkell 1933, p. 36).

After Vaughan's death the zones were further modified by S. H. Reynolds (1926), and the Vaughan–Reynolds scheme was for many years accepted as the standard of reference for correlation in the limestone facies of the British Lower Carboniferous. Meanwhile the upper part of the Lower Carboniferous in the shaly facies was being zoned by goniatites. Correlation between the fwo facies was not easy and could only be partially established through areas in the Pennines where the facies alternate. The coral-brachiopod scheme, being older, tended to be regarded as the standard with which the goniatite succession must be correlated, although being founded on benthonic fossils it is less precise than a scheme based on the pelagic goniatites. In 1926 a group of geologists from the north of England, in a minority report of a British Association committee set up to try to obtain agreement as to the meaning to be attached to Lower Carboniferous zonal terms, made some scathing remarks about coral-brachiopod stratigraphy: 'We have urged . . . the desirability of defining zones in terms of faunal lists . . . and were prepared to supply such lists for the

Culm [i.e. shale] phase. We understand, however, that there are difficulties in the way of this procedure in the case of the coral-brachiopod phase, the faunas being either too ill-defined or composed of undescribed forms . . . The absence of such definitions in the coral-brachiopod phase was largely the cause of the confusion which this Committee was set up to rectify, and if confusion is to be avoided in the future, in our opinion much greater precision in the definition of coral zones will be required' (*in* Hudson, 1926). This is a surprising statement to find after twenty years of intensive work on the coral-brachiopod zones, and makes a serious accusation of failure to define the zones adequately. It may have contained a germ of truth, but it had little effect on the general acceptance of the Vaughan–Reynolds scheme.

The scheme came to be seriously questioned when the Geological Survey in 1938 started to re-map the Carboniferous Limestone of the Bristol district. Detailed lithological mapping within the limestone, which was carried out for the first time, showed that some of the fossils on which Vaughan had founded his zones were facies fossils whose presence was correlated with the existence of a certain rock type in highly variable lithology (Fig. 17). Other fossils showed great variations in their vertical ranges even over a short distance in the same lithology. The field geologists of the Survey found Vaughan's zonal scheme unworkable for local correlation of different facies within the Carboniferous Limestone, and did not adopt it as a descriptive framework for their maps. They used instead the lithostratigraphical subdivisions which had been in use before Vaughan proposed his zones.

T. N. George (1958) protested strongly at the cavalier treatment which the scheme received at the hands of the Survey and while he accepted much criticism of the zones as fair he regarded their total rejection as a retrograde step. Any correlation in the limestone facies of the Lower Carboniferous must depend on corals and brachiopods, and these fossils undergo evolutionary changes which, if they can be properly understood and defined, can be used for stratigraphical purposes. Indeed the value of Vaughan's scheme is demonstrated by the considerable advances in Lower Carboniferous stratigraphy made during the last sixty years as a result of its use. It is likely that in the first flush of enthusiasm after Vaughan's 1905 paper too much was expected, and local variations of abundance of species, due to accidents of facies, may have been given too much importance. It may also be that the evolution of the fauna cannot sustain the detailed division into subzones and horizons which Vaughan made. It is certain that confusion occurred as a result of the definition of some horizons and boundaries in different ways by different workers, and Vaughan himself was inconsistent. These are now matters of history and should not be allowed to hinder acceptance of a workable scheme. A further serious difficulty when Vaughan started work was the lack of sufficiently rigorous palaeontological studies of many of the fossils. Vaughan tried to offset this by providing notes and illustrations of some of the important species, but even twenty years later, as noted above, much descriptive work remained to be done. From this point of view Vaughan may have been ahead of his time in attempting to make a zonal scheme with inadequate palaeontological tools.

The present trend is to retain in modified form the zones of Vaughan and Reynolds while abandoning most of the smaller subdivisions. Such a scheme has been proposed by George (1958, p. 240):

Viséan Stage	⎰	*Dibunophyllum* Zone (D)
		Seminula Zone (S_2)
	⎱	Upper *Caninia* Zone (C_2S_1)
Tournaisian Stage	⎰	Lower *Caninia* Zone (C_1)
		Zaphrentis Zone (Z)
	⎱	*Cleistopora* Zone (K)

It must be emphasized that the zones are assemblage zones and the fossils which give their names to the zones are merely convenient labels. Vaughan's original zonal names for K and S_2 are retained although the fossil names have been changed: the corals identified as *Cleistopora* (a Devonian genus) are now known as *Vaughania*, and the brachiopods identified as *Seminula* by Vaughan are now referred to *Composita*.

Such a simplified system can be used with some confidence although even George admits that the Tournaisian zones can be applied only in parts of south-west England. It provides a much less refined subdivision than, for example, the trilobite zones of the Upper Cambrian (p. 37) or the ammonoid zones of the Jurassic and Cretaceous, but is the best that can be achieved at present.

SENONIAN AMMONITE ZONES OF THE GULF COAST, USA

The Austin Chalk comprises about 350 feet of limestones which have a more or less continuous outcrop through Texas and neighbouring states. It is currently regarded as a group divided into six formations on lithological grounds, although the lithology varies in detail along the outcrop. The first attempt to provide a zonal sequence based on ammonoids was made by W. S. Adkins and published in 1933. This proved unsatisfactory because the ammonites were never fully described, being named mainly with reference to European species. Keith Young (1963) has produced a new zonal scheme (Fig. 7) supported by full descriptions of the fossils. Ammonites are relatively rare and sporadic in occurrence in the Austin Group. Young was unable to recognize biozones since the total number of specimens available (often a dozen or two, sometimes less) of most of the species was so small that the observed vertical ranges are unlikely to represent the duration of existence of the species, even locally, and he was also unable to work out phylogenetic relationships. He therefore described assemblage zones and listed the complete fauna of each zone, some of the species being restricted to the zone and others not. Some of the ranges shown in Figure 7 had to be postulated; for example, *Priono-cycloceras gabrielense*, a zonal index, has not so far been collected at the same locality as any other ammonite species. It has been found above beds with *Peroniceras* and below beds with *Texanites stangeri densicostatus*. Other ammonites which have been found in the same interval are grouped with it to characterize an assemblage zone.

The lowest zone, of *Peroniceras haasi*, is named after the only ammonite to occur in the lowest beds of the Austin group apart from *Coilopoceras austinense* which had been used as an index by Adkins. Young's scheme is based wholly on collignoniceratids and this was presumably the reason for changing the index. The base of the Westphalicum Zone was placed at the entry of the index species. Young only examined seven individuals of the species from the Austin Group, and further finds could extend its range at any time. Only one other species, *P. moureti*, is recorded definitely from the zone. The Gabrielense Zone has already been mentioned in the last paragraph. The Densicostatus Zone is defined by the range of the index fossil which is relatively common, about 25 examples being known from the Austin Group. *Texanites americanus*, said to appear first near the top of the zone, is unlikely to be useful in defining the zone since it is long-ranging and appears to be rare.

Texanites texanus is the index species of a well-known European zone but only seven specimens are known from the type area of Texas. It is the only member of the assemblage restricted to the zone. According to the range diagram (Fig. 7) the zone has been arbitrarily extended upwards to the base of formation C. Presumably, as with other index species, the range of *T. texanus* may be extended at any time by further field work. Although the next zonal index, *T.t. gallica*, is shown in Young's diagram as ranging throughout the zone named after it, only one specimen of this subspecies is known from Texas and its locality and horizon are not recorded. It is believed by Young to come from formation C on the evidence of its matrix and such a position is also said to accord with evolutionary development in *Texanites*. No other species are definitely known to be characteristic of this zone, although several are tentatively assigned to it.

The base of the Shiloensis Zone coincides with the base of the Dessau Formation and with the first appearance of the index species which is relatively common (20 good specimens). The base of the zone is also marked by the first appearance of *Bevahites bevahensis* and several other ammonoid species, and of the oyster *Exogyra ponderosa*, and is one of the best defined levels in this succession. It is likely, of course, that the sudden appearance of a number of species resulted from some change of conditions marked by the change of lithology at the base of the Dessau Formation, and is without significance outside the area of occurrence of this formation. Moreover if the base of the formation should be diachronic (which is unknown) then the entry of the fossils would presumably vary in age accordingly.

Submortoniceras tequesquitense, index species of the next zone,

D

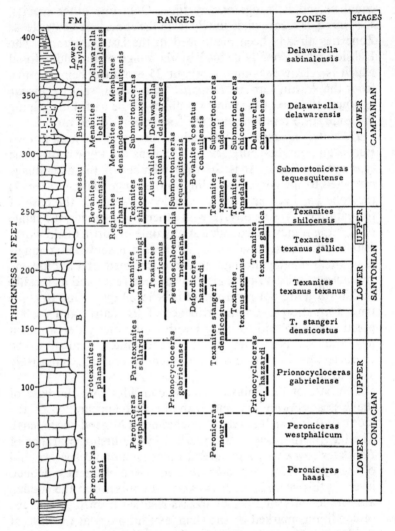

Fig. 7. Ranges, known (continuous lines) and inferred (broken lines), of collignoniceratid ammonite species in the Austin Chalk of Central Texas, and the zonal scheme based upon them. FM = formation. From Young (1963).

is a comparatively abundant fossil in the upper part of the Dessau Formation, accompanied by about 25 other ammonoid and lamellibranch species some of which are restricted to the zone or to part of it. This is the most fossiliferous level in the Austin Group and the zone appears to be securely founded. There is a marked change in fauna at the junction with the zone of *Delawarella delawarensis*, a number of species becoming locally extinct and others making a sudden appearance. About 17 species besides the index are listed definitely from the Delawarensis Zone and a number of them are restricted to the zone. This is the highest zone of the Austin Group. In the overlying Taylor Formation fossils are again rare, and a zone has been named after the only ammonite, *Delawarella sabinalensis*, of which four specimens are known.

The lowest seven zones (Haasi to Shiloensis) are stated by Young to be assemblage zones, but in fact hardly any diagnostic species occur besides the index species. Most of these are rare and future collecting could extend their vertical ranges. The zones are really teilzones, a term used for zones based on locally observed ranges of fossils which do not necessarily coincide with their total ranges in geological time (p. 55). The highest two zones of the Austin Group are genuine assemblage zones.

One asks oneself whether in his desire to provide adequate biostratigraphical subdivision Young has not stretched the evidence too far. His study has certainly improved the dating of the Austin Group in terms of the internationally recognized stages Coniacian, Santonian and Campanian. But the setting up of a zone such as the Gallica Zone, based on a single specimen of which the horizon is not known, runs counter to the principles of choosing zonal fossils as generally agreed and as expounded later in this chapter. In fairness I must add that the basis of the zones is clearly explained by Young, allowing the analysis presented above.

SUBDIVISIONS OF THE RARICOSTATUM ZONE

The ammonite zones of the Lower Jurassic of north-west Europe are based principally on the evolution of the fossils concerned, but in many points of detail are arbitrary or depend on local migration. An example is the division into subzones of the Raricostatum Zone in Britain:

Raricostatum Zone
{
Aplanatum Subzone
Macdonnelli „
Raricostatum „
Densinodulum „
}

The zone as a whole is characterized by ammonites of the family Echioceratidae, but the earliest members (*Palaeoechioceras*) occur sporadically in the underlying Oxynotum Zone. The base of the Raricostatum Zone is marked by the appearance of *Crucilobiceras*, an ammonite unrelated to the Echioceratidae, the species *C. densinodulum* giving its name to the lowest subzone. The reason for this is historical, beds with *Crucilobiceras* having been included in the Raricostatum Zone by Oppel in 1856. *Crucilobiceras* is accompanied by sundry echioceratids including the keeled, bisulcate genus *Paltechioceras* and by some ammonites which survive from the Oxynotum Zone.

Higher in the zone the species *Echioceras raricostatum* makes a sudden appearance. Its range defines the Raricostatum Subzone, and although it also gives its name to the zone this is nothing more than a convenient label, for the genus *Echioceras* is not found in the two upper subzones. The bisulcate genus *Paltechioceras* is not found in the Raricostatum Subzone although it reappears higher up.

The entry into the succession of the genus *Leptechioceras*, a compressed form often with loss of ornament on the outer whorls, marks the base of the subzone named after *L. macdonnelli*. The subzone is defined by the range of *Leptechioceras*. *Paltechioceras* also occurs in the subzone and so does *Neomicroceras*, a probable descendant of *Crucilobiceras* with simplified suture-lines.

At the top of the zone, between the highest *Leptechioceras* and the lowest ammonites of the succeeding Jamesoni Zone, is an interval with *Paltechioceras* and sundry long-ranging ammonites of other families. This is the Aplanatum Subzone. The index species *P. aplanatum* is probably restricted to the subzone, but the latter is in practice defined as the part of the succession between the Macdonnelli Subzone and the base of the Jamesoni Zone.

Subdivision of the Raricostatum Zone is thus seen to depend on the sudden appearance first of *Echioceras* and then of *Leptechioceras*. It is possible that each of these genera in turn evolved rapidly from the long-ranging *Paltechioceras*, and that the intermediate stages have not yet been found. It is equally possible that the actual appearances of these genera are the result of migration into the area. The subzones are teilzones rather than biozones. The consistent succession of genera within the zone, which is the same at a number of sections in different parts of the country, gives practical confirmation of the reliability of the subzones.

CHARACTERISTICS OF ZONAL FOSSILS

We may now generalize concerning the attributes of zonal fossils. It is often said that a good zone fossil should have a short range in time, a wide geographical distribution, be reasonably common and easily recognizable. We may consider these in turn, and we shall find that there are exceptions to all.

The desirability of reasonable abundance is obvious. An *Archaeopteryx* Zone would be of little practical value. Frequently one must be prepared for a good deal of collecting before diagnostic species are found in a succession. The British Corallian Beds are zoned by ammonites, but these are never common; as a result of long-continued collecting by several workers, most Corallian formations can be placed in the zonal scheme, but the casual searcher for ammonites will often be disappointed. Fossils are seldom uniformly abundant at all levels of a succession, and may occur only at widely spaced horizons, as in many outcrops of graptolitic black shales. In general, however, unless a fossil is reasonably common we can never be sure that our collecting has really established its vertical range in a section, and accurate observations of vertical range are the foundation of all good zonal schemes.

Ease of identification is probably the desideratum which is least often fulfilled. It is inevitable that increasing refinement of stratigraphic subdivision should depend on finer and finer palaeontological distinctions, and that these should result from the work of experts with long experience of particular fossil groups. This trend is often deplored by field geologists but it is essential to stratigraphical progress, and its practical importance is sufficiently proved by the use of fine palaeontological zoning in coalfield geology, oil drilling and other economic fields. Few people would venture to identify Coal Measures lamellibranchs, graptolites, or Foraminifera, to name only a few examples. In any case, there are few zonal schemes for which well-illustrated accounts of the diagnostic species are available.

A small vertical range is the essential feature of a good zonal fossil. It may arise in various ways. In the case exemplified by some of the Upper Cambrian subzones (p. 39) the vertical range is short because the species is part of a rapidly evolving lineage, and is separated from its ancestors and descendants by evolutionary changes. Where fossil collecting shows that such a lineage was evolving in an area, we can be reasonably sure that we are dealing with the whole of the time-range of a species. The brachiopod zones of the English Cornbrash (p. 114) probably represent short local periods of abundance of the index species, whose total ranges in time may have been longer. They are locally useful but not of general validity.

The fineness of subdivision which is possible depends, of course, on the fossils available, and detailed zonal schemes cannot always be set up. In the case of the Carboniferous Limestone (p. 41) the corals and brachiopods were evolving slowly, and attempts to distinguish small subdivisions have not proved successful.

The geographical ranges of zonal fossils will be discussed later in this chapter. The relative importance of the chief fossil groups for zoning in different geological systems is shown in Figure 8.

KINDS OF ZONE

For a zone defined by the whole or absolute range of a species, genus or other taxon, S. S. Buckman in 1902 proposed the term *biozone*. The more explicit term *range-zone* is equally acceptable. Thus the trilobite subzones of the Upper Cambrian are largely biozones, as explained above.

If the occurrence of a fossil is isolated in time, so to speak, and we cannot recognize ancestral or descendant species in the same area, then we do not know whether the range determined by our collecting represents the whole duration of existence of the species, or only part of it. For a zone defined by part of the total range, represented by the local occurrence of a species, the term *teilzone* was suggested by Pompeckj (1914). It is a German word (*teil* = part) which has been used in English as there is no simple translation. Some of the zones of the Austin Chalk are likely to be made up of teilzones rather than biozones, since the number of specimens available are too few to establish the true ranges of the species. It is clear that biozones are better than teilzones, for the distance over which they can be used for correlation is limited only by the geographical distribution of the zonal fossils, assuming that evolutionary changes are simultaneous throughout the area. The factors which determine the

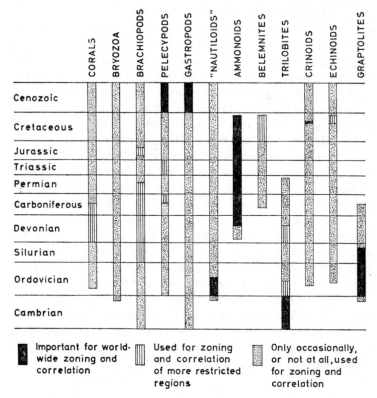

FIG. 8. Table showing the relative importance for zonal purposes of certain groups of invertebrate macrofossils. Modified from Teichert (1958).

ranges of species in teilzones are likely to be local, and it is unlikely that schemes of teilzones will be applicable over great distances, or that a teilzone index fossil found a long way from the area in which the scheme is applicable will necessarily denote contemporaneity with its zone in the type area.

Arkell (1933, p. 33) wrote 'unfortunately opportunities for making use of lineages in zonal work are extremely rare'. They are not, perhaps, as rare as all that, but the fact is that most zonal schemes were not intentionally based on lineages when they were first set up, although some have become so based as a result of later revision. Authors seldom state explicitly the basis for their zones. When the index fossils of successive zones belong to different genera or higher taxonomic groups, one may suspect that the zones are teilzones. This is not invariably so: the nomenclature of the Lower Jurassic zonal and subzonal ammonites conceals a good deal of evolutionary sequence. When several index species have the same generic name they may turn out to be members of a lineage, but only enquiry into their palaeontology will show whether they are or not.

Buckman (1902) proposed the term *faunizone* for a zone defined by a number of species, such as the zones of the English Chalk. *Assemblage-zone*, used by the American Commission on Stratigraphical Nomenclature, is more explicit. Since the individual species which make up the fauna will have different vertical ranges it is not to be expected that a succession of faunizones will have precise zonal boundaries. They will rather be vague and ill-defined, or transitional as one fauna replaces another. Many graptolite zones appear to be faunizones, the whole assemblage being characteristic; individual species, sometimes even index species, may occur in more than one zone. The zones of the Carboniferous Limestone offer another example.

Numerous other terms for different kinds of zone have been invented. A few recent ones were reviewed by Teichert (1957, 1958). The use of all these terms is almost entirely confined to discussions of stratigraphical principles. They do not normally form parts of the names of actual zones.

SUBDIVISIONS OF THE ZONE

I have said that the zone is universally accepted as the unit of biostratigraphical subdivision. However, in some, perhaps at present a minority, of zonal schemes, where very detailed subdivision has been possible, the real units are *subzones*, which are grouped into zones with anything from two to five or six to a zone. This is the case with the Upper Cambrian already reviewed, and with the Lower Jurassic of north-west Europe. In the Lower Jurassic the reason is historical. The zones are largely those of Oppel, the founder of Jurassic zones. As further study gave rise to finer subdivision zones were multiplied until a very large number had been named. L. F. Spath, revising the Lower Jurassic zones in 1942, returned largely to Oppel's zones, dividing most of them into subzones. In this case, as with the Upper Cambrian, many of the subzones approximate to biozones of species, while some zones are biozones of genera, and others are defined arbitrarily in terms of the included subzones. It could be argued in these cases that the subzones ought to be called zones, and certainly there is no uniformity of usage. It would not be difficult to find, in other parts of the stratigraphic column, zones whose basis and extent are similar to those of the Jurassic subzones. Yet the Lower Jurassic zones, by recognition of characteristic genera or general faunal resemblance, often permit correlation when evidence is inadequate for subzones to be identified, and practical experience justifies current usage.

The term *zonule* was proposed by C. L. and M. A. Fenton in 1928, but has been used less than subzone. For some workers it is a smaller and more local subdivision than a subzone. The American Commission on Stratigraphic Nomenclature (1961) accepts both subzone and zonule, the latter being a very small subdivision which may be distinguished without dividing the whole zone into subzones. *Horizon* has been used in much the same sense in Britain.

NOMENCLATURE OF ZONES

It is general practice to name a zone after a single fossil species, the index species. More than one species may be necessary to define the zone but still it is convenient to have a short name which recalls some salient faunal characteristic. Occasionally zones have been named after two or more fossils, such as the

Zone of *Berriasella ciliata* and *Anavirgatites palmatus* at the top of the Lower Tithonian, but there seems to be no need for this so long as it is recognized that the name is only a name and does not have to be a definition or description. Generic names have sometimes been used alone, for example in the Upper Devonian (Manticoceras Zone), but it is common practice to designate an index species even when the zone is in fact defined by the range of the genus. In a few cases zones based on assemblages have been given consecutive letters or numbers instead of names. The Lower Palaeozoic of the Oslo region in Norway is divided into series numbered from 1 to 10. Within each series the stages are referred to by roman letters and substages by greek letters. So we have a 1aα, 1aβ, 1bγ and so on. Pollen zones in the Late-Glacial and Postglacial are referred to by roman numerals. Use of letters or numbers suffers from the disadvantage that if a new zone is established it cannot be inserted. Some people believe that following the conventions of zoological nomenclature the specific name should be printed in italics with a small initial letter, thus: *extensus* Zone. Others have felt that since the specific name has become part of a zone name it is permissible and preferable to write Extensus Zone. The name of the index species may also be written in full, in which case the problem is avoided. Thus *Didymograptus extensus* Zone, Zone of *D. extensus*, *extensus* Zone and Extensus Zone all mean the same thing.

Some zonal schemes have abbreviated designations, often the initial letters of index fossils. Thus the goniatite zones used in the lower part of the British Upper Carboniferous proposed by W. S. Bisat in 1924 were designated E, H, R and G, after *Eumorphoceras*, *Homoceras*, *Reticuloceras* and *Gastrioceras*. Similarly Vaughan labelled his Carboniferous Limestone zones K, Z, C, S and D, as shown on page 42.

EVOLUTIONARY BASIS OF ZONES

I have said that correlation by members of an evolving lineage is very precise because the evolutionary changes can be considered as simultaneous everywhere. I must now try to justify this statement. To do so we must examine the way in which evolution takes place. A living species is made up of a number of local communities or populations, each a group of inter-breeding individuals. The populations form, at any instant of time, a more or less continuous geographical distribution. More or less, because there may be local temporary breaks in the distribution, but provided that they do not last too long the identity of the species will be preserved throughout its distribution. Permanent breaks in the distribution may result in the separated parts pursuing different courses of evolution, and evolving into different subspecies and then species. We will assume for the moment that this does not happen Within each local population interbreeding and natural selection keep the variation within the population within fairly narrow limits. At this point, however, we must enter a qualification: environmental conditions may vary between the areas occupied by the local populations, and so the factors influencing selection will be slightly different for each Often certain factors, such as temperature, altitude (of land) or depth (of water) vary in a regular way, showing a steady change in one direction across the area of distribution. Natural selection of forms best fitted for the different conditions in different parts of the distribution produces slight differences between adjacent populations, which are maintained even though the populations can interbreed. In the case of a regular gradation in conditions, as mentioned above, a species may show a regular gradation in some of its characters, and the difference between individuals from opposite ends of the distribution may be considerable This gradation is called a *cline*, and many examples are known from living species: they are the rule rather than the exception in widely distributed species. Most known clines have been demonstrated in land animals; for example, in Africa Burchell's zebra in the southern part of its distribution shows a progressive reduction of stripes, starting with the tail and legs and then, further south, on the body, the extreme form of this cline being the now extinct quagga which has often been regarded as a separate species. Many examples are known from birds, probably because they are attractive objects of study. Fewer examples are known from marine animals, which are more difficult to observe.

The very existence of clines shows that there is continuity of interbreeding throughout the geographical range of the species; if a species is unvarying, the same conclusion holds. Coming now to evolutionary changes, it is clear that we must conceive them occurring throughout the distribution of a species. With the minor exceptions due to the existence of clines, the same mutations are being thrown up, and the same, or similar selective processes are operating on them throughout the distribution. The species as a whole evolves, and not just one part of it in one place. If this is accepted, it is clear that homotaxis of members of evolving lineages does indicate contemporaneity, for all parts of the distribution pass through the same evolutionary stage at the same time.

ZONAL PROVINCES

Most zonal schemes are restricted to certain areas or provinces, outside which the characteristic fossils do not occur. It is the exception for a living species to have a world-wide distribution, and the same was true in the past.

One could expect planktonic and pelagic animals to have the widest distributions. In fact such organisms at the present day show great differences in this respect, exemplified by Figure 9 which compares the pelagic gastropods *Clio pyramidata*, which has a world-wide distribution within latitudes 40°S and 60°N, and *Limacina helicina*, restricted to the North Pacific and North Atlantic. The graptolites, which are believed to have been planktonic, show comparable differences: a few species have a more or less world-wide distribution, but the majority are much more restricted. O. M. B. Bulman has recently plotted the distribution of *Nemagraptus gracilis* (Fig. 10) which has been recorded from every continent except Africa. He points out that the present distribution of the species shows a wide range of latitude, from about 40°S to 75°N, which is unusual in living planktonic species, but that if pole positions for the Ordovician provided by palaeomagnetic data are accepted the distribution lies in the tropical zone, and would be comparable with that shown in Figure 9B. Some, at least, of the ammonoids may have been pelagic or planktonic. They and the graptolites are generally reckoned to be among the most useful fossils for zoning (Fig. 8). An example of an ammonoid family with a restricted distribution, the Jurassic Cardioceratidae, is shown in Figure 10. If changes of pole positions suggested by palaeo-

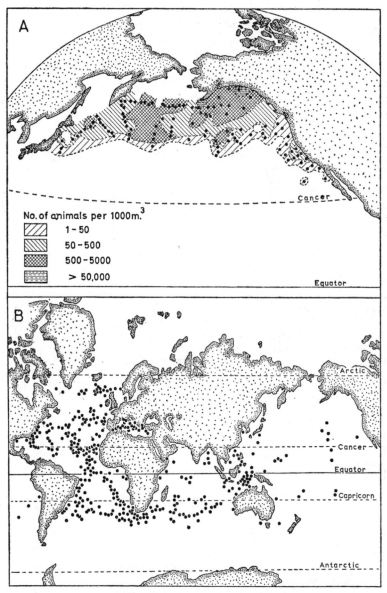

FIG. 9. Distributions of two living species of pelagic pteropods. A, *Limacina helicina* in the north Pacific (it also occurs in the north Atlantic). B, *Clio pyramidata*. After McGowan (1963) and Ekman (1935).

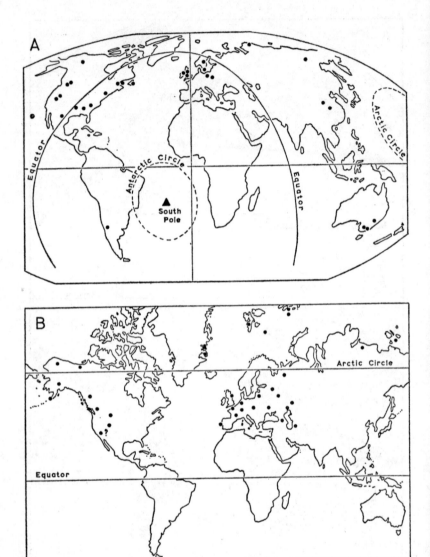

FIG. 10. A, distribution of the Ordovician graptolite *Nemagraptus gracilis*. The positions of the south pole, polar circles and equator in mid-Ordovician time, worked out from European palaeomagnetic data, are shown. B, distribution of ammonites of the family Cardioceratidae in the Callovian and Lower Oxfordian Stages of the Jurassic. After Bulman (1964) and Arkell (1956).

magnetism are accepted, the geographical range would have lain further south than it does now.

The pelagic Foraminifera also are extensively used for correlation, especially in Cainozoic rocks, but many species are long-ranging and the degree of precision obtainable does not seem to approach that possible with trilobites, graptolites or ammonoids.

Benthonic animals can hardly achieve such wide distributions, as there is virtually nothing in common between the shallow and the deep sea fauna. Even though benthonic species may have wide distributions they are likely to be restricted to certain habitats and therefore, if they are preserved as fossils, to certain facies, like the coral-brachiopod fauna with which Vaughan zoned the limestone facies of the English Lower Carboniferous.

The geographical limits of the zonal schemes described earlier in this chapter have already been mentioned. As an example of the development of faunal (and zonal) provinces the Jurassic of the northern hemisphere may be studied, as particularly exemplified by the correlation of the Arctic and North-west European Provinces.

Lower Jurassic ammonite genera had, on the whole, a very wide distribution. Forms originally described in Europe can be recognized in North and South America, East Greenland, the USSR, Japan and other circum-Pacific islands. The most complete sequence is known from Europe but other occurrences can often be correlated with the European zonal scheme. At the beginning of the Middle Jurassic, however, we suddenly begin to find in Spitzbergen, East Greenland, North America and Northern Asia ammonites which have no counterparts in Europe. It seems that with regression of the seas the distribution of previously widespread groups became split up, and locally isolated populations began to follow different evolutionary lines. The uniformity of Lower Jurassic ammonites was replaced by a number of local faunas, and there now have to be different zonal schemes in different regions. The comparison between the Arctic Province, exemplified by East Greenland, and North-west Europe is shown diagrammatically in Figure 11. Throughout the Bajocian and Bathonian Stages the faunas remained distinct and the zonal schemes based upon them can only be correlated approximately. The separation was ended

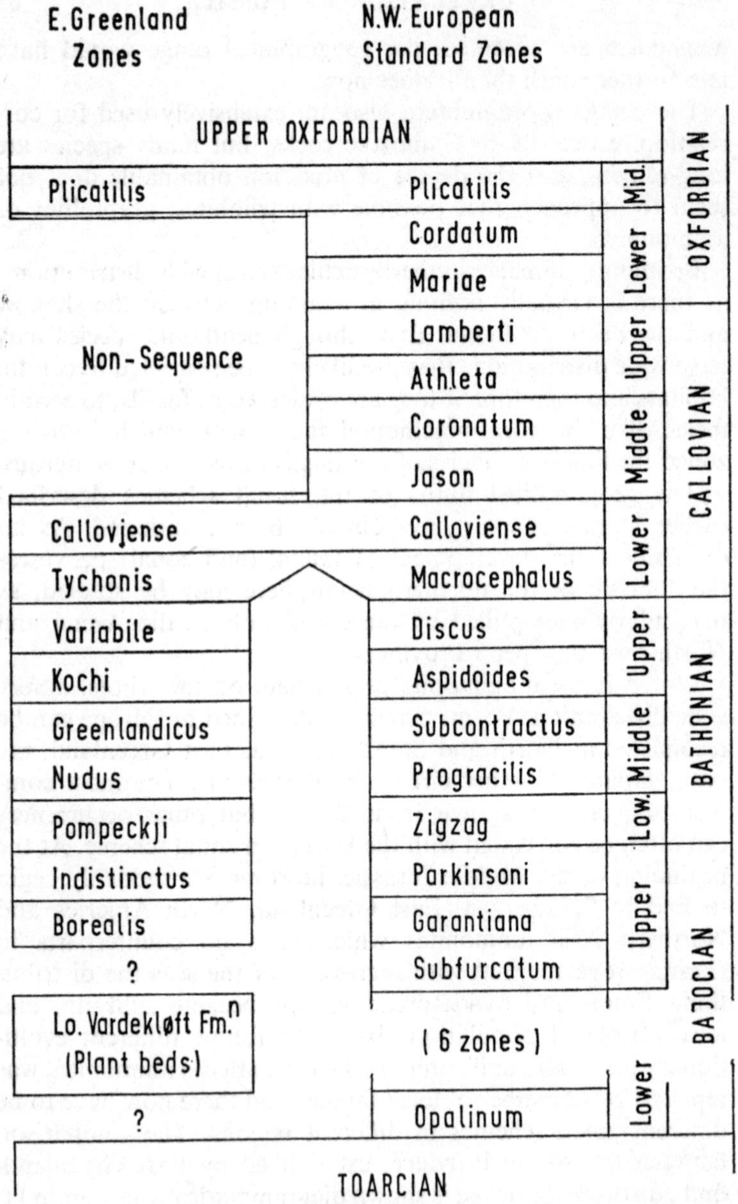

E.Greenland Zones	N.W. European Standard Zones		
UPPER OXFORDIAN			OXFORDIAN
Plicatilis	Plicatilis	Mid.	OXFORDIAN
	Cordatum	Lower	OXFORDIAN
	Mariae	Lower	OXFORDIAN
Non-Sequence	Lamberti	Upper	CALLOVIAN
	Athleta	Upper	CALLOVIAN
	Coronatum	Middle	CALLOVIAN
	Jason	Middle	CALLOVIAN
Callovjense	Calloviense	Lower	CALLOVIAN
Tychonis	Macrocephalus	Lower	CALLOVIAN
Variabile	Discus	Upper	BATHONIAN
Kochi	Aspidoides	Upper	BATHONIAN
Greenlandicus	Subcontractus	Middle	BATHONIAN
Nudus	Progracilis	Middle	BATHONIAN
Pompeckji	Zigzag	Low.	BATHONIAN
Indistinctus	Parkinsoni	Upper	BAJOCIAN
Borealis	Garantiana	Upper	BAJOCIAN
?	Subfurcatum	Upper	BAJOCIAN
Lo. Vardekløft Fm.^{n} (Plant beds)	(6 zones)		BAJOCIAN
?	Opalinum	Lower	BAJOCIAN
TOARCIAN			

Fig. 11. Comparison of ammonite zones for part of the Jurassic System of East Greenland and north-west Europe. After Callomon (1963).

during the Lower Callovian by the migration of the Arctic fauna into northern Europe, after which the ammonites are very similar again and correlation is easy. The *macrocephalus* fauna, which was displaced from northern Europe by the Arctic *calloviense* fauna, retreated southwards during the Lower Callovian and continued to exist in the Mediterranean area.

An interesting lesson is to be learned by comparing the ammonites just described with the lamellibranchs. The ammonites evolved faster and soon after isolation became quite different in the two provinces. The lamellibranchs, with slower rates of evolution, did not diverge and Middle Jurassic bivalves from Greenland all belong to genera found in northern Europe, and many to European species. They are, however, almost useless for correlation since the species have such long ranges —many persist through about half the Jurassic System with hardly any change at all.

In the late Cretaceous a number of local ammonoid zonal schemes are in use and correlation between them gives rise to many problems. With reference to his scheme for the Gulf Coast area (p. 48), Young has written 'The zones of the Rocky Mountain region are entirely different from those of equivalent strata in Texas, within the Senonian, and correlation can be estimated only by the mutual occurrence of unusual fossils. The zones of the standard European sequence cannot be set up in Texas with any great accuracy. Instead, a parallel zonation must be set up in each area, and a correlation estimated on rarely occurring fossils, stage of evolution, homotaxial superposition of family and generic groups, and intuition'. In the western interior of the United States a very detailed zonation of the Senonian (Coniacian to Maestrichtian stages) has been set up on the basis of scaphitid and baculitid ammonoids, about 35 zones being recognized. It is likely that some of these 'zones' correspond in scale to subzones, or even smaller units, in, for example, the Scandinavian Upper Cambrian or the European Jurassic. Some of the zones can be recognized in other areas where the same groups of ammonoids occur, such as West Greenland, but in general the zones are of local application only and correlation with other areas is in general terms, being open to a good deal of doubt at some horizons.

Another example of faunal provinces is found in the Lower

E

Cambrian. The so-called Atlantic Province includes outcrops in Britain (except north-west Scotland), Scandinavia, Poland, Germany, south-eastern Newfoundland, Nova Scotia and the neighbourhood of Boston (Mass.), and is characterized by a sequence of trilobite faunas by which correlations can be made within the province. The so-called Pacific Province, including north-west Scotland, East Greenland, north-western Newfoundland, the St. Lawrence valley, and the Appalachians, has a different set of trilobites, no genus being common to the two provinces. Direct correlation is thus impossible. An alternation of faunas from the two provinces has been found in north-western Greenland, and a mixture of genera from the two provinces occurs at one horizon in New York State, and by such slender but valuable indications some progress has been made in correlating 'Atlantic' and 'Pacific' zones.

CORRELATION BETWEEN DIFFERENT FACIES

Difficulties similar to those met with in correlating two faunal provinces recur in the correlation of groups of rocks which though contemporaneous, carry different fossils because they are of different facies (p. 111). Correlation must be made in one of three ways: either by fossils which are common to the two facies, or by study of sections in which the facies alternate, or in which fossils of the two facies occur together—so-called mixed facies. A classic example of the problem is provided by the shelly and graptolitic facies of the British Ordovician and Silurian. The pure graptolitic facies consists of black shales and greywackes with no fossils other than graptolites, while the shelly includes a wide range of rock types with trilobites and brachiopods as the dominant fossils but no graptolites. Direct correlation is impossible, and for long the equivalence of zones in the shelly and graptolitic facies was uncertain. Progress was eventually made by the discovery of formations containing a 'mixed' fauna, both graptolites and shallow-water shelly fossils being present. The tendency for a long time was to regard the graptolite zones as forming a standard with which other facies were correlated as far as possible; more recently a series of shelly zones, based mainly on trilobites and brachiopods, has been recognized in its own right.

The same problem is encountered in correlating marine and non-marine sediments. Major problems of this kind occur throughout the Upper Palaeozoic, the Devonian, Carboniferous, and Permian all having widespread and sometimes economically important non-marine rocks. It is most unlikely that any fossils will be common to both marine and non-marine deposits, or, since most marine animals can tolerate very little reduction of salinity, that intermediate regions such as estuaries will be of much use. We have, therefore, to rely on places where marine and non-marine rocks alternate in the vertical succession. Fortunately these are not entirely lacking. Some correlation of marine Devonian with the continental Old Red Sandstone facies can be made from alternating facies in Belgium and south-west Britain, while the non-marine Coal Measures, of the European Upper Carboniferous, are interrupted by marine bands some of which appear to be of almost continent-wide extent. In both cases general equivalence can be suggested but detailed correlation is unknown and may never be achieved. In the case of the Permian of England, the barren non-marine beds can only be dated as earlier or later than the marine Magnesian Limestone which forms the middle part of the system.

STAGES

When accurate zonal correlation is impossible more general equivalence may often be proved. I have already mentioned d'Orbigny's stages. Although the hypothesis of a fauna of world-wide distribution, created everywhere at the same moment, is no longer accepted, the stage is still a valid unit of correlation. D'Orbigny's claim that very few fossil species are found in more than one stage is still largely true. A fossil fauna can often, therefore, be placed in its correct stage even if it cannot be correlated with an individual zone. Correlation of the Palaeogene of the Anglo-French area is almost exclusively in terms of stages.

Stages often form a convenient framework if the development of a system is to be examined on a world-wide scale. They were so used successfully by Arkell in the *Jurassic Geology of the World* (1956). Taking subdivision of the Jurassic into ten stages as his standard, he was able to place almost all known outcrops in the stages, in spite of the fact that various zonal schemes are in local use. Only towards the end of the Jurassic, when differentiation into faunal provinces such as has been described for the middle Jurassic (p. 63) again occurred, was he forced to recognize stages of less than world-wide applicability (Portlandian of north-west Europe, Tithonian of the Mediterranean belt and its extensions, Volgian of Russia), and recent research gives reason to believe that even these may soon be dispensed with.

In many systems more or less world-wide correlation of marine strata can be achieved in terms of stages. There is not always agreement as to what scheme of stages should be used, but that is another matter: experience leads one to believe that in due course—knowledge in some systems is more advanced than in others—marine stages of general applicability could be set up for all systems. Meanwhile, local schemes of subdivision at stage (or series) level are still in use in some systems: for example, in the Ordovician which is discussed further on page 154. Russian geologists accept the lowest three European Carboniferous stages, but have five marine stages of their own for the rest of the system.

Difficulties of correlating non-marine strata have been mentioned above. Where such rocks are of limited extent they are usually correlated with marine stages as far as possible: for example, the Deltaic Series of the Jurassic of north-east England which can be assigned to the Bajocian and Bathonian Stages by means of intercalated marine beds. Where extensive non-marine rocks occur independent stages may be set up for them. The Old Red Sandstone of the Anglo-Welsh borderland has been divided into the Downtonian, Dittonian, Breconian and Farlovian Stages on the basis of ostracoderms. There is an unconformity between the Breconian and the Farlovian, but deposition occurred during this interval of time in north-east Scotland and has been referred to the Orcadian Stage. Another example is given by the Continental Cainozoic rocks of North America, which have been divided into 19 stages on the basis of land mammals.

CORRELATION DIAGRAMS

Correlation of formations within a system or other substantial unit over a large area may be shown in a table, an example being shown in Figure 12. The vertical scale represents time and is marked off in biostratigraphical units: series, stages or zones. As the duration of these units in years is not usually known they are made of arbitrary size: either all the same, or variable depending on the amount of detail to be included at different levels. The areas to be correlated may be each allotted a column, as in Figure 12, or the known or conjectured lateral changes may be indicated as in Figure 24. In the former case symbols may be used to show the different lithologies present, but one must remember that thicknesses cannot be shown, the apparent thickness of each unit in the diagram being determined by the number of zones which it includes.

DURATION OF STRATIGRAPHICAL UNITS

The actual time in years represented by the deposition of stratigraphical units does not much concern stratigraphers in their day-to-day work. It is, however, of interest for several reasons. In the case of biostratigraphical units, it is important for the arguments concerning the contemporaneity of biostratigraphical boundaries, already reviewed on page 32, and it affords the only means we have of comparing the degree of subdivision which has been achieved in different parts of the stratigraphical column. In the case of formations it is of interest to know how long particular conditions persisted; for example, the conditions under which the European Chalk was laid down must have lasted almost unchanged in some areas for about 30 million years.

The only reliable evidence is provided by radiometric ages. These can seldom be obtained for rocks on the boundaries of stratigraphical units, and the ages of these must be obtained by interpolation. In the case of many systems there are comparatively few reliable ages, and we can only expect to get figures which are a general indication of duration of units. In the most recent symposium on the Phanerozoic time-scale (Harland and others, 1964) many contributors have first interpolated the ages of system boundaries, and then arbitrarily subdivided the resulting period of time to obtain dates for stage boundaries, so that two stages of approximation are

SERIES	STAGE	FAUNAL ZONES [37] Compiler → / Overlying →	Napah Range, California [38] J.F.Mason / Ordovician	Eastern Grand Canyon, Arizona [39] C.E.Resser and E.D.McKee / Carboniferous	Western Grand Canyon, Arizona [40] E.T.Schenk and H.E.Wheeler / Devonian	Southeastern Arizona [41] Stoyanow, Wheeler, and Kerr / Devonian	Eureka District, Nevada [42] J. Bridge / Ordovician	Desert Range, Nevada [43] J.F. / Ordovician
UPPER CAMBRIAN	TREMPEALEAUAN	Plethopeltis zone			Dolomites and limestones, possibly Upper Cambrian; formation not named	Rincon limestone ?	Pogonip limestone (Lower part only)	(Genera of both faunas occur together)
		Saukiella-Colvinella zone (Saukiella subzone / Colvinella subzone)						
		Upper Dikelocephalus zone (D. gracilis)				Copper Queen formation	(* Goodwin ls of Walcott in part)	(Formations not yet named)
		Platycolpus-Scosvogyra zone						
		Dikelocephalus postrectus zone						
		Briscoia zone						
		Prosaukia-Ptychaspis zone (Prosaukia subzone / Ptychaspis subzone)						
		Conaspis zone (Taonicephalus subzone / Eoorthis subzone)						
	FRANCONIAN	Ptychopleurites zone	Nopah fm.				Dunderberg "shale" (Basal fauna may be pre-Elvinia)	
		Elvinia zone						
	DRESBACHIAN	Aphelaspis zone				Pepper Sauce Canyon sandstone	(Probable position of Hamburg dol.; no fossils; exact position not known)	
		Crepicephalus zone						
		Cedaria zone				Abrigo limestone		
MIDDLE CAMBRIAN (STAGES NOT YET SATISFACTORILY DEFINED)		Deissella - Centropleura vermontensis zone [1]					Secret Canyon shale	(Faunas unstudied; probably similar to those of Nopah Range)
		Fatella-Thomsanopsis zone						
		Olenoides-Orria-Marjumia zone	Cornfield Springs formation		Mead limestone	Cochise formation	Geddes limestone	
		Elrathiella-Triplagnostus-Clasopsis zone (Elrathiella-Triplagnostus subzone / Clasopsis subzone)					(Approximate position of Eldorado dolomite; no fossils, exact age unknown.)	
		Bolaspis-Glyphaspis zone	Bonanza King formation		Peasley limestone	Pima formation (fossils of uncertain exact age)		
		Glossopleura-Kootenia zone	Cadiz formation	Muav-limestone				
		Zacanthoides-Anoria zone			Chisholm shale	Bolsa quartzite		
		Albertella zone	(Fauna may be older than indicated)	Bright Angel shale	Lyndon fm.			
		Kochaspis liliana zone						
LOWER CAMBRIAN (STAGES NOT YET ESTABLISHED)		Syspacephalus zone	Wood Canyon formation [2]	Wood Canyon formation	Pioche shale		Ploche formation	(Faunas unstudied; probably similar to those of Nopah Range. An Olenellus and a Nevadia fauna occur in Palmetto Range.)
		Olenellus zone						
		Bonnia zone			Prospect Mtn. quartzite		Prospect Mountain quartzite	
		Obolella zone	Stirling quartzite [3] [4]					
		Underlying →	Archean and Proterozoic? tillite	Beltian and Archean	Archean	Apache	Pre-Cambrian	Base not seen

FIG. 12. Part of a correlation table for the Cambrian of North America. From Howell and others (1944). Vertical ruling indicates absence of strata.

involved. The following table has been obtained by working out the average length of time represented by a series, stage or zone over a whole system, except where otherwise stated. The figures are in millions of years and the table is based on the information in Harland and others (1964).

System	Average length of			Notes
	Series	Stage	Zone	
Oligocene	—	6	—	Averages for European marine stages. North American mammal stages average about 3.
Eocene	—	4	—	
Paleocene	—	6	—	
Cretaceous	—	6	1	Ammonoid zones.
Jurassic	—	6	1	
Trias	—	4	1	
Permian	—	11	1	Stages range from 5 to 15 according to one interpretation of radiometric data.
Carboniferous	—	(a) 13 (b) 6·5	(c) 3 (d) 0·6	(a) European stages. These range from 5 to 20 according to one interpretation of radiometric data. (b) North American stages. (c) Non-marine lamellibranch zones in Westphalian. (d) Goniatite Zones in Namurian.
Devonian	—	7	(e) 1	Stages range from 4 to 16 according to estimates based on maximum thicknesses of sediment. (e) Goniatite zones in Famennian. In earlier stages zones are longer.
Silurian	13	—	2	Graptolite zones. Locally zones about 1 m.y. long may be distinguished.
Ordovician	11	1	(f) 4½	Bancroft's stages of the Caradoc (p. 153). (f) Graptolite zones.
Cambrian	—	—	2	Trilobite zones in U. Cambrian of Scandinavia. Trilobite zones in Lower and Middle Cambrian probably longer.

Various estimates suggest that within any one system subdivisions of the same category are likely to vary in duration with a ratio of longest to shortest of about 4 : 1. Thus Mesozoic ammonite zones are likely to be from $\frac{1}{2}$ to 2 million years long, although a few doubtless fall outside these limits. Although we must not lose sight of this variation, some interesting conclusions can be drawn from the table. It is remarkable that ammonoid zones of the Devonian (Famennian), Permian and Mesozoic all average about 1 million years in length. Some of these zones can be divided into subzones which are likely to be from $\frac{1}{4}$ to $\frac{1}{2}$ million years long, and this may be the shortest length of time which can be normally distinguished by means of ammonoids. Graptolite zones on average are longer than ammonoid zones. Strachan (in Harland and others 1964) reckoned that an Ordovician graptolite zone was about equal to a Jurassic stage. Upper Cambrian trilobite zones are about equal to Silurian graptolite zones. The Upper Cambrian zones are divided into subzones of comparable length (average $\frac{1}{2}$ million years) to ammonoid subzones in the Mesozoic.

Stages of Mesozoic and Cainozoic Systems are remarkably constant in their average duration. In the European Palaeozoic, except for the Devonian which is more like the Mesozoic in its scale of subdivision, the main subdivisions, whether called stages or series, have averages between 11 and 13 million years. This shows that it is merely custom that determines that these subdivisions are known as series in some cases and stages in others. The greater length of Palaeozoic stages as compared with Mesozoic ones may be related to the greater length of Palaeozoic zones. The number of zones to a stage in the Palaeozoic, although highly variable, appears to average the same as in the Mesozoic, about five.

The geological periods show less variation in length than smaller units. In the Palaeozoic and Mesozoic, the range is from 32·5 million years (Trias) to 71 million years (Cretaceous), a ratio of only about 1 : 2·2, while for the whole of the Phanerozoic, if we ignore the traditional periods of the Cainozoic (Palaeocene, Eocene, etc.) and accept Paleogene and Neogene as periods, the range is only about 1 : 2·7.

3

LITHOLOGICAL CORRELATION

THE first two chapters have shown that the study of sedimentary sequences involves two distinct processes: the tracing of the lithological succession and its variations, and the attempt to establish time-divisions usually by means of fossils. When time-divisions can be recognized they often show formations to be of variable age or diachronous (p. 119), and one of their functions is to correlate different rocks of the same age. Nevertheless, in certain rather special circumstances rock-units may help with time correlation when fossils fail.

Many bedding planes may be isochronous surfaces. In normal marine sedimentation intervals between successive increments of sediment give rise to discontinuities which eventually become bedding planes. Such intervals are likely to be ultimately caused by climatic factors which are uniform over a small area, and the resultant bedding planes will be isochronous. Even if this is so, individual beds or bedding-planes cannot usually be traced for any great distance. There are rare exceptions. R. A. Fairbairn (1966) has studied the Great Limestone in the Limestone Group of the Carboniferous in Weardale, County Durham, England, and has found that a whole succession of individual beds within the 80-foot-thick formation can be traced for a dozen miles or more, each retaining its individuality and remaining recognizable despite certain changes: some of the beds, for example, pass through a coralline facies. It seems likely that each bed is of the same age throughout its lateral extent. In the case of the correlation of the English Chalk by electric well-logs, mentioned later in this chapter (p. 86), the marker bands which are used run roughly parallel to one another and there is some likelihood that each resulted from some general cause affecting sedimentation simultaneously throughout the area. In other cases the principle is clearly invalid. In false-bedded sediments the major bedding planes are unlikely to be iso-chronous, but presumably get younger in the direction towards which the oblique beds are building up.

If we have a bed due to some unusual cause, sandwiched between rocks of more ordinary type, we may be able to recognize it easily, and if we have reason to think that the cause operated simultaneously throughout the area, we can use the bed for correlation. Such a bed might result from a volcanic eruption producing clouds of ash which are dispersed in the atmosphere and finally sink to rest on the sea bed, forming an intercalation in the marine sequence. Volcanic eruptions are often repeated, and if there are a number of bands their use-fulness vanishes unless we can identify individual ones. We may be able to do this petrologically, or by proving the continuity of individual beds by mapping. The clays known as *bentonites*, composed largely of the clay-minerals montmorillonite and illite, are thought to have resulted from the decomposition of layers of volcanic ash, and have been used for correlation with apparent success.

M. N. Bramlette and W. W. Rubey, mapping Upper Creta-ceous rocks on the boundary between Montana and Wyoming, found that they could trace some bentonites over a distance of more than 25 miles, and used them to decipher a region of rapidly changing lithology (Fig. 13). Several of their bentonites were distinctive, as indicated by names such as Gray-red Bentonite and Biotite Bentonite. With their aid Bramlette and Rubey showed that the Belle Fourche Shale represents a longer period of time in the west than it does in the east, where the upper part passes laterally into limestone. In theory very long range correlations might be made as a result of eruptions like that of Krakatoa in 1883, dust-clouds from which had a world-wide distribution. They do not seem to have been achieved so far: probably the deposit resulting from a dust cloud a long way from its source is usually too thin to be easily recognized. In practice correlation is within limited areas (usually <100 miles across) over which the ash beds are thick enough to be conspicuous.

Another rock-type which has been used is evaporite, which often occurs in sequences of red beds barren of fossils, where correlation is exceptionally difficult. The assumption is that

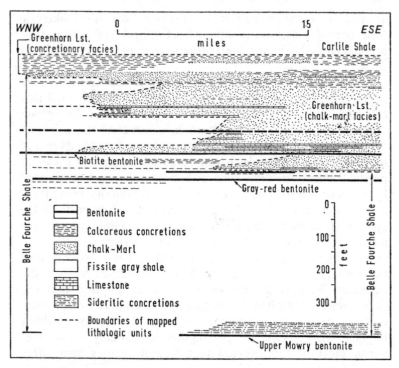

WNW   0   15   ESE
—Greenhorn Lst.   miles
(concretionary facies)   Carlile Shale

Greenhorn·Lst.
(chalk-marl facies)

Biotite bentonite

Gray-red bentonite

Belle Fourche Shale

	Bentonite
	Calcareous concretions
	Chalk-Marl
	Fissile gray shale.
	Limestone
	Sideritic concretions
- - - -	Boundaries of mapped lithologic units

0
100
200
300
feet

Belle Fourche Shale

Upper Mowry bentonite

FIG. 13. Section of Upper Cretaceous rocks in south-eastern Montana and north-eastern Wyoming, U.S.A. Isochronous horizons provided by bentonites show that the upper part of the Belle Fourche Shale in the west passes eastwards into Greenhorn Limestone. Based on mapping by M. N. Bramlette and W. W. Rubey, after Moore (1949).

within a single basin of evaporation any one evaporite bed will be of roughly the same time-range everywhere, although as evaporation proceeds the basin may shrink or expand, according to the supply of brine and tectonic changes. For an expanding basin, the base of the evaporite will not be of the same age everywhere; for a contracting one, the same will apply to the top. In general, evaporite deposits are lenticular; the thickest parts represent longer periods of evaporation than the edges, and the base or the top or both will be of variable age. Whether this variation in age is much greater than the errors involved in correlation by fossils we do not know.

It is clear, however, that thin evaporites, which are likely to have been the result of relatively brief episodes of evaporation, are likely to be better for correlation than thick, lenticular ones.

S. E. Hollingworth (1942) maintained that evaporites could be regarded as part of a sedimentary cycle, and claimed that two such cycles, and part of a third, were traceable throughout much of the Permo-Trias of Yorkshire and Durham, England. 'Taking the succession of evaporites and associated beds east of the Pennines as a whole, it can be expressed as two cycles of partial desiccation—limestone, anhydrite, salt—each terminated by an incursion of clastic sediments . . .' Within one basin there is a strong reason to believe that corresponding parts of the cycle, in different places, are of the same age. Hollingworth also identified the same cycles in the detached outcrop of the Vale of Eden, which accumulated in a separate basin divided from the Yorkshire-Durham area by the Carboniferous rocks of the Pennines. This correlation involves the assumption that the cycles were controlled by variations in climate which were uniform over such a comparatively small area as northern England. In this case the assumption is probably reasonable, but it must be remembered that tectonic causes also affect depositional cycles.

The correlation of rhythmic or cyclic sequences will be considered in the next section. The methods of varve analysis have also been applied to evaporites, and will be mentioned again later in the chapter.

CORRELATION OF RHYTHMIC SEQUENCES

Wheelton Hind (1896) recognized that the greater part of the British Carboniferous 'consists of recurring series of sandstones, clays, coals, and limestones, indicating clearly a repeated oscillation of level, with intervening periods of rest, during which the terrestrial conditions necessary for the growth of the coal flora obtained'. Recurrent sedimentary cycles were later recognized in the Pennsylvanian (Upper Carboniferous) of North America, and were named *cyclothems* by H. R. Wanless and J. M. Weller (1932). An example of a cyclothem from the British Coal Measures is:

Coal Seam
Seatearth (representing the soil in which the coal flora grew)
Sandstone
Alternating siltstone and mudstone in thin layers
Mudstone
Marine Band

The clastic sediments represent the filling up of an area to water-level, and the coal seam was formed from the vegetation which colonized the area during a stable period after silting-up had been completed. Repeated cyclothems are therefore likely to have been controlled by intermittent subsidence, or possibly by steady subsidence accompanied by eustatic changes in sea level. Individual cyclothems vary and a part, often the marine band at the base or the coal at the top, may be absent. The marine band may contain a varied fauna including goniatites, valuable for correlation, and generally passes up into brackish-water beds characterized by a more restricted fauna with forms such as *Lingula*. There follow beds with non-marine lamellibranchs, while the upper part of the cyclothem is characterized by fossil plants. Palaeontological zoning has been attempted on the basis of three groups of fossils: goniatites, non-marine lamellibranchs, and plants. The goniatites, although valuable for correlation when they occur, are of restricted use because of the absence of the marine band from many cyclothems. The non-marine lamellibranchs were studied intensively in Britain by Wheelton Hind, and later by A. E. Trueman and others. A set of six zones was set up by J. H. Davies and A. E. Trueman in 1927 for the British Coal Measures. Trueman (1946) explained that 'The zones . . . depend mainly on the entry of new forms and the disappearance of earlier groups. They are not primarily based on evolutionary changes . . .'. There are considerable palaeontological difficulties, due (among other things) to the great individual variation shown by these sessile lamellibranchs, and to their sporadic occurrence and often poor preservation. For a while this zonal scheme seemed to be of great promise, but recently its value for detailed correlation has been found to be limited. In the South Wales Coalfield, for example, the *Anthraconauta phillipsii* Zone includes about 13 cyclothems. Fossil plants, once used as the principal basis for subdivision of the Coal Measures, have also gradually declined in importance. Most of the plant species are long-ranging and the boundaries between the zones are hard to define. The floras of individual seams are not easy to distinguish.

These remarks show that the palaeontological zoning available in coal measures sequences is coarse in comparison with the detailed lithological subdivision and does not provide the precise correlation required for economic purposes. For these purposes, lithological correlation is, in fact, needed; the mining engineer has to identify a seam in the sequence so as to estimate how many workable seams lie below it, and at what depths. Provided that some part of the cyclothem, such as a marine band or coal seam, can be identified, the rest falls into place. Moreover if some cyclothems in a sequence can be correlated the ones in between fall into place. Caution is necessary because cyclothems may wedge out, but in general good correlation can be obtained. The Geological Survey of Great Britain correlates Coal Measures sequences in this way, with stress on marine bands for primary correlation and on various peculiarities of the cyclothems for detailed correlation. Several marine bands, and several coal seams, can be traced through a number of coalfields and some British marine bands have also been identified on the continent of Europe: for example, the band known as the Dukinfield or Mansfield on the flanks of the Pennines has been correlated with Skipsey's Marine Band in Scotland, the Cefn Coed in South Wales and the Aegir of Westphalia. The Clay Cross Marine Band of the East Pennine Coalfield has been correlated with the Amman of South Wales, the Poissonière of northern France and the Catharina of Westphalia. Thus the broad features of the sequence of cyclothems are the same throughout Britain and perhaps throughout a larger area of Europe. Locally there are many variations, and two or more coal seams may unite, presumably as a result of local warping and non-deposition of the clastic parts of some cyclothems.

In North America, likewise, coal seams have been traced over considerable distances. The Herrin Coal of South Illinois and its equivalents have been traced over an area of at least 10,000 square miles.

Is this correlation in the sense that the coal seams and marine bands represent isochronous surfaces? Wheelton Hind (1896) did not think so: he visualized facies belts migrating across Britain, so that at one instant coal might be accumulating in one place while a marine band was being laid down elsewhere. A. E. Trueman, on the other hand, thought that 'Each seam appears to reflect the existence of coal-forming conditions simultaneously over a very wide area . . . a seam does not appear to be markedly diachronic and cannot be interpreted as representing a . . . gradual advance of a belt of vegetation across the area in question' (1946). It is difficult to decide between these two views because palaeontological correlation, as shown above, is not sensitive enough.

There are limits to the diachronism which could occur. The fossil contents of each of the principal marine bands show close and detailed similarity wherever the band occurs, and some contain diagnostic goniatites. Even if a marine band is diachronic its range in age could not have been greater than that of the characteristic goniatite. I have suggested above (p. 72) that the average duration of an ammonoid zone was about 1 million years, and the limit to possible diachronism of Coal Measures cyclothems is likely to be of this order. At a rough estimate there are more than 70 cyclothems in British Coal Measures and the average length of a cyclothem is about 0·35 million years.

The number of cyclothems in the Pennsylvanian of the USA is of the same order as the number in the British Upper Carboniferous. In the type area of the Pennsylvanian a total of 81 has been identified (Branson 1962, p. 109). H. R. Wanless and F. P. Shepard (1936) have developed the theory that the cyclothems were controlled by eustatic and therefore world-wide changes in sea level, possibly as a result of variations in the amount of land ice. If they are right (others have maintained that only a few exceptional cyclothems reflect world-wide causes) there should be a possibility of eventual detailed correlation in the Carboniferous on a world-wide scale.

Correlation by *tonstein* horizons is important in the Westphalian coalfield. The word, which literally means 'claystone', has come to be used in German, French and English to signify a claystone in which the clay mineral is almost exclusively kaolinite. Bands of such rock, usually only a few inches thick, are found within or close to coal seams and thus belong to the terrestrial part of the coal measures cyclothem. There have been various theories as to their origin; L. R. Moore has recently suggested that they result from soil-forming processes. Some of these bands can be identified over wide areas by mineralogical features.

The use of tonsteins for correlation has been developed in the coalfields of northern Europe from the Pas de Calais to Westphalia, to supplement the rare marine bands, and about ten tonsteins have been recognized as extending throughout this area, others having a more local distribution. In British coalfields tonsteins remained unrecognized until the early 1960s. About ten have now been identified in the coalfields of the Midlands, but have not yet been correlated with the continental ones. They have also been found in coal-bearing rocks in several other areas.

The value of tonsteins is comparable with that of marine bands. The tonsteins run parallel to the cyclothems and do not offer an independent means of correlation. They are complementary to the other methods of correlating coal measures sequences.

A method of lithological correlation dependant on the presence of annual layers of sediment is varve analysis. Varved sediments first attracted attention in Sweden where they were deposited by the melt waters of the receding glaciers of the Pleistocene glaciation. The spring melt water, which contains much matter in suspension, drops the coarser particles first while the finer ones settle more slowly, so that each year is represented by a distinct layer showing graded bedding. Swedish varves range from about 1 metre to less than 1 cm thick. This seasonal rhythm was first understood by Högbom (1889), but the chief name associated with varve analysis is that of G. de Geer. Varve correlation depends on the fact that the annual layers are not all identical, but vary in thickness and other characters as a result of climatic variations from year to year. The simplest method identifies varves by relative thickness. Graphical methods are used to compare different sections and unusually thick or thin varves or distinctive groups are correlated. The process suffers from the same disadvantages as other methods involving comparison of sequences: because climatic changes tend to repeat themselves after some kind of cyclical pattern, there is a danger that similar parts of different cycles will be correlated by mistake. Errors are least when neighbouring sections are compared, and most liable to occur in long-distance correlations. The classic varve theory was expounded by de Geer (1940) and by G. Arrhenius (1947). M. Sauramo in Finland refined de Geer's method by comparing other sedimentary characters as well as thickness.

Detailed schemes of varve chronology have been built up in Scandinavia by de Geer and his followers, in North America by E. Antevs, in Patagonia and Chile by C. C. Z. Caldenius. De Geer adopted as a datum the Bipartition, or splitting of the Swedish ice-cap into two, which he identified with a thick varve, due to release of dammed-up meltwater, which can be recognized in many sections. The age of the Bipartition has been worked out by varve counts as 6,839 BC, and a detailed chronology of Scandinavian Late-glacial and Post-glacial retreat-stages has been built up. The earliest date obtainable is about 13,000 years BC.

The methods of varve analysis have been applied in a few cases to pre-Pleistocene rocks. Annual layers may not be very uncommon in sediments, but we cannot often prove them to be annual and even less frequently can we use them for correlation. Thin laminae in the Lower Lias of southern England and in the Cretaceous of the Black Hills of South Dakota have been shown to be probably annual by A. Hallam (1960) and W. W. Rubey (1931) respectively. Each lamina is marked by a concentration of carbonaceous material which is explained as due to an annual cycle in the abundance of plankton. An extensive series of supposed annual laminae occurs in the Upper Devonian and Lower Carboniferous of Thuringia, where counts of exposed sections, extrapolated through more than 6,500 feet of sediments, gave a maximum duration of about 740,000 years for the lower half of the Viséan Stage of the Carboniferous (Korn 1938). This is ridiculously short compared with the estimated length of the Carboniferous on the radiometric time-scale (p. 97). Presumably there are many non-sequences in Thuringia; alternatively the layers may not have been annual, or the extrapolation may be in error.

Evaporites often show regular banding and J. A. Udden (1924), G. Richter-Bernburg (1964) and others have thought

F

these bands, which range in thickness from about 15 cm to less than a millimetre, to be annual varves. Richter-Bernburg has applied methods similar to de Geer's to the evaporite sequence in the Permian Zechstein basin of north Germany. Here, as with the Viséan of Thuringia, the duration of evaporite formation which is obtained, about 0·5 million years, is short viewed in the context of geological time. D. B. Smith has recently observed (in Harland and others 1964, p. 215)

'Attempts made during the preparation of this paper to relate thicknesses to rates of sedimentation were unsuccessful . . . The Permian system, with its wealth of laminated and banded rocks, appears to be particularly suitable for such attempts . . . In almost every case investigated, however, it is found that if the cycles are [assumed to be] annual, then their deposition occupied only a small part (in some cases less than a tenth) of the time suggested by isotopic datings. From this it follows that either the bands represent more than one year or that unrecognized hiatuses occur between bands or between larger sedimentary units. This introduces so many uncertainties that estimates of the time represented by such beds are of little value.'

Correlation of climatic sequences recorded by alternations of different types of deposit, fauna or flora, or even by geomorphological evidence, has long been employed by workers on the Pleistocene. Needless to say corresponding points must be recognizable in both sequences. Even so there is much room for error, since a local sequence may be incomplete. In its most undesirable form, climatic correlation has led workers who could recognize four glacial phases in their own areas to correlate them with the four classic alpine glaciations, Günz, Mindel, Riss and Würm.

Correlation of climatic phases is being checked as knowledge of the Pleistocene faunal and floral changes increases, and in the late Pleistocene radiocarbon dating is now used. Nevertheless it remains an important method in Pleistocene correlation.

BOREHOLE LOGS

Boreholes drilled for research are usually cored, and provide a complete lithological section hardly to be obtained in any other way. Commercial boreholes are sometimes cored, for example when samples of coal or ore are wanted for analysis, or if macrofossils are wanted for correlation. Most of them, however, are drilled by methods which bring the rock to the surface as small cuttings. Large-scale textures and structures are never seen, and macrofossils are not recovered. It may also be difficult to determine the exact depth of lithological changes, and rapid alternations of lithology may be blurred due to mixing of cuttings as they ascend in the drilling mud. These deficiencies are partly compensated for by specialized methods of logging which are not applicable to surface outcrops.

Two of the most commonly used are the resistivity and self-potential logs, which are usually measured and recorded at the same time by lowering down the hole an instrument called a sonde containing the appropriate electrodes. The electrical resistance of dry rock is very high and the current which a rock will pass depends on the fluids in the pore-spaces of the rocks. The fluid is often salt water in which case porous rocks such as sands or sandstones will show low resistivity while impermeable ones such as shale, limestone or salt will give high resistivity. Oil and gas are poor conductors and high resistivity may also be due to their presence in a porous rock. As the sonde is lowered past different beds the current flowing to it changes with the resistivity of the beds which it is passing. A continuous graph showing the variation of resistance with depth is drawn by an automatic recorder at the surface. Refinements have been devised to give greater detail. Various electrode spacings may be used, and in general more closely-spaced electrodes result in a more detailed log. The Microlog, which measures resistance between electrodes only an inch or two apart, produces a very detailed curve but has certain disadvantages, one of which is that it is influenced by the thickness of the mud cake on the borehole wall. It is common practice, therefore, to record several resistivity logs with different electrode spacings. Further information may be obtained by comparing these logs (Bullerwell 1964).

Self-potential is due to electric currents set up by electrolytic action between the drilling mud and solutions in the pore spaces of the rocks, and is measured between an electrode fixed at the surface and another in the sonde. As the latter passes different beds natural potentials up to about 100 millivolts are observed. The resultant graph, again automatically recorded, is a straight line when the electrode is opposite impermeable beds, but is deflected when permeable rocks are passed. The deflections are positive if the fluid in the pores is less saline than the drilling mud, and negative in the opposite case. Since both the self-potential and resistivity logs depend on the properties of the fluid in permeable beds, there is usually a general correspondence between the two, and a rapid inspection of them will reveal the chief groups of permeable and impermeable beds in the bore-hole.

The gamma ray log is made by a Geiger-Müller or a scintillation counter which measures the natural radioactivity of the rocks. This is due to the presence of traces of radioactive minerals and is generally greater for shales than for other common rocks. High readings therefore indicate shales and sometimes individual beds can be distinguished from others by their characteristic level of radioactivity.

Another radioactivity log is the neutron log, in which the rock is bombarded with neutrons from an artificial source. The bombardment causes emission of gamma rays, the intensity of which is measured, as for the gamma ray log. This intensity is inversely proportional to the concentration of hydrogen atoms in the rock, which is dependent on the amount of liquid present: water and oil have similar hydrogen atom concentrations, which are much higher than those of normal rock. The neutron log, like the resistivity and self-potential logs, is thus mainly responsive to changes in permeability. Radioactivity logs have the advantage over resistivity and self-potential logs that they can be applied to boreholes which have been lined with steel casing, and may thus be made in old boreholes which were drilled and lined before modern logging methods were in general use. The resistivity and self-potential logs must be made before the hole is lined.

Electrical and gamma ray logs can be used in conjunction with information from cuttings and other data to make the lithological section of the hole more precise. A valuable feature of these logs, however, is the ease with which they can be compared directly by eye (Fig. 14). It has become the practice in many cases to publish them alongside lithological sections of

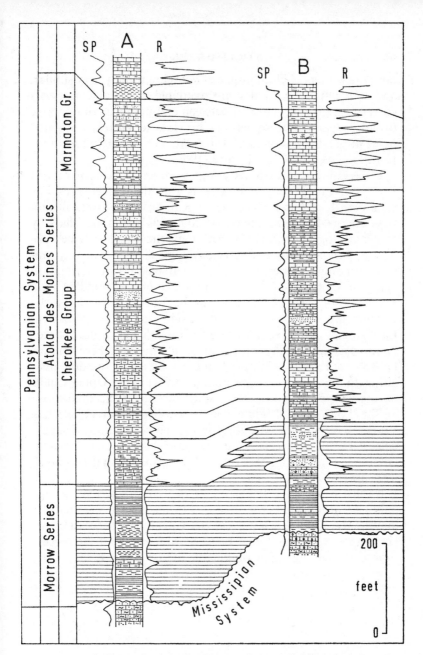

FIG. 14. Lithological and electric logs of two wells about 20 miles apart through the Upper Carboniferous (Pennsylvanian) of Colorado, U.S.A. SP = self-potential, R = resistivity. Note the general correspondence between the peaks of the two resistivity logs. The correlation indicated assumes that the basal Pennsylvanian black shale (Morrow Series) is diachronous and in well B replaces the lowest subdivision of the Cherokee Group of well A. After Rascoe (1962).

boreholes. Logs of closely-spaced holes are usually very similar, and if a number of holes are available at suitable intervals correlation may be achieved between end-points a considerable distance apart. It is sometimes possible to correlate isolated holes at greater distances. A full treatment of logging methods has been given by C. A. Moore (1963).

Electrical and radioactivity logs were developed for oilfield work but are finding applications outside this sphere. For example, D. A. Gray of the Geological Survey of Great Britain has developed a method of correlating beds within the Chalk by resistivity logs (Gray 1965). Although the Chalk can be sub-divided lithologically and palaeontologically, its relatively uniform lithology renders any additional method of correlation valuable. Gray found that within the Lower and Middle Chalk ten resistivity marker bands can be traced throughout the London area, and the same succession can be recognized in East Anglia and Lincolnshire even though individual marker bands may fail locally with change of lithology. Five marker bands were recognized in the Upper Chalk of the London area, although the influence of the abundant flint in the Upper Chalk on the resistivity makes these bands more variable than those in the Lower and Middle Chalk. R. McQuillin (1964) has studied the use of electric logging for the correlation of superficial deposits, and found that good correlations could often be obtained in the glacial drift of Cheshire provided that boreholes were closely spaced.

It must be remembered that electrical and radioactivity logs only give lithological correlation, with the limitations that this may imply. They do, however, enable complex successions to be compared with ease, and they record facts about the succession which are not easily obtainable in any other way.

4

RADIOMETRIC DATING

THE stratigraphical scale in common use for fossiliferous Phanerozoic rocks is relative. Each unit is defined by its relationship to the units above and below, and 'dating' a rock formation means putting it in its correct place in the sequence by correlation with rocks whose position is already known. The actual duration in years of parts of the scale is not of primary importance for many applications of stratigraphy and for a long time there was no reliable evidence on the point. For other purposes, however, such as the study of geological processes, some idea of the time involved is valuable, and igneous and metamorphic rocks cannot be dated on the stratigraphical scale unless their age can be related to that of a sedimentary rock of known position. For these reasons geologists have always been keenly interested in estimating the ages in years of the various stratigraphical subdivisions. The only hope of doing so lies in measuring the effect of some process which has been operating, during the period of time in question, at a rate which is known or can be estimated. Three processes have received serious study: the accumulation of salt in the oceans; the accumulation of the sedimentary rocks; and the accumulation of the decay products of radioactive minerals.

The possibility of using radioactivity to measure the ages of minerals was pointed out by Lord Ernest Rutherford in lectures in 1904 and 1905, and in 1907 B. B. Boltwood in the USA published the first estimate of geological age, based on uranium: lead ratios from published analyses of minerals. He obtained an age of around 1,600 millions of years for some of the Laurentian rocks of the Canadian Shield. In the following year R. J. Strutt (1908), working in Britain, published figures based on the amount of helium present in radioactive minerals, obtaining 141 millions of years for a Carboniferous mineral. The dates obtained were epoch-making because they indicated the order of magnitude of geological time, but the method remained of little practical use to stratigraphers. The major achievement of the early years of work in the field was Arthur Holmes' establishment, by skilful interpolation based on sedimentary thicknesses between a few age determinations, of a time scale which has since been altered surprisingly little in its major features.

The 1939–1945 war produced a great increase in knowledge of radioactive substances, and ways of measuring radioactivity were refined. More or less concurrently the mass spectrometer was being improved by A. O. Nier, enabling the isotopic composition of an element to be found accurately. For the first time radiometric dating of large numbers of samples became practical, and several laboratories were equipped for the work. The results have already revolutionized Pre-Cambrian stratigraphy.

In principle the method is very simple. A radioactive element changes or *decays* spontaneously into another, more stable substance, the change being accompanied by the emission of energy as radiation. The rate of decay can be measured experimentally. It has been found to be unaffected by external factors such as temperature and pressure, and the rate for any substance is believed to have been unvarying throughout geological time. This last assumption forms the basis of radiometric dating. If we can analyse a radioactive mineral and find the proportion of unaltered material to the decay product, and if we know its rate of decay, then we can calculate the age of the mineral, provided that nothing has been added or removed since the mineral was formed.

The rate of decay is governed by a law which states that the number of atoms which disintegrate in unit time $-\left(\dfrac{dN}{dt}\right)$ is proportional to the total number of atoms present, N;

$$-\frac{dN}{dt} = \lambda N$$

where λ is the *decay constant* for the substance under consideration. The number of atoms, N_o, at t years ago is found by integrating the first equation to

$$N = N_o e^{-\lambda t}$$

$$\text{or} \quad N_o = N e^{\lambda t}$$

e being the base of natural logarithms.

In practice the rate of decay is often defined by the *half-life*, which is the time required for half the original mass of radio-active atoms to disintegrate. The half-life T is related simply to the decay constant:

$$T = \frac{0 \cdot 6931}{\lambda}$$

To find the age of a substance (t) we must consider another quantity, the number of atoms of the decay product which have been formed, which we call N_d (we do not, of course, know what N_o was). We can then say

$$N_d = N_o - N = N(e^{\lambda t} - 1),$$

hence $\quad \dfrac{N_d}{N} = (e^{\lambda t} - 1)$

and $\quad t = \dfrac{1}{\lambda \, \mathrm{loge}\left(1 + \dfrac{N_d}{N}\right)}$

In practice there are numerous difficulties. Some of the decay products may have been lost through leaching or diffusion. Alternatively, material indistinguishable from the decay product may have been initially present in addition to that produced by radioactive decay. The amounts of radioactive minerals present in rocks are usually very small, which adds to the practical difficulties of separation and analysis. Much of the work involves distinguishing between different isotopes of the same element with a mass spectrometer which is a very expensive instrument. On account of the experimental difficulties and expense of the work it has been carried on at comparatively few laboratories.

There are, of course, geological difficulties also. A radio-metric date gives the age of an element or mineral, which is not necessarily the age of the rock in which it occurs. Metamorphism or mineralization may have affected the rock and it is often these events that are dated rather than the original formation;

alternatively, a mineral may be older than the rock in which it now occurs. Now that a number of different methods are available (see below), these may give different ages when applied to the same rock. This is not so distressing as it may seem, for it may enable different episodes in the history of the rock to be elucidated. Although the sources of error mentioned above (and others) still cause serious difficulty, the accumulation of experience has enabled geologists working on age determinations to evaluate the likely errors in the different methods, and to compensate for them to some extent.

When radioactivity was discovered by Becquerel in 1896 it appeared to be an exceptional phenomenon peculiar to one or two elements. We now know that many elements have radioactive isotopes, any of which could in theory be used for dating. Various considerations determine the elements which are useful in practice. The half-life of the element should be comparable with the age to be measured: if it is much shorter or longer the proportion of parent element or end-product present will be very small and small errors in analysis will cause large errors in the calculated age. Half-lives range from a fraction of a millisecond to more than 10^{10} years, and for a particular purpose only a few elements fall within the desired range. Then the elements must be present in sufficient quantity, and methods for analysing them must be available. In many cases dating would not be difficult if one could obtain a large quantity of uncontaminated radioactive material plus decay product. In practice much technical skill is involved in working with very small concentrations of material and eliminating sources of error.

The first minerals to be used for radioactive dating were uranium and thorium. Two radioactive isotopes of uranium, U^{235} and U^{238}, and one of thorium Th ^{232}, have been used. In all these cases the decay is not a simple change, but the decay product is itself radioactive and proceeds to decompose further and the process is repeated a number of times until an inert end product is formed. The full sequence for U^{235} is given at the top of the opposite page.

a-particles are helium nuclei and β-particles are electrons. For practical purposes all but the first and last members of this

Isotope	Particle emitted	Half-life of isotope	
(start) U^{235}	α	$7 \cdot 13 \times 10^8$	years
Th^{231}	β	$25 \cdot 6$	hours
Pa^{231}	α	$3 \cdot 43 \times 10^4$	years
Ac^{227}	β	$13 \cdot 5$	years
Th^{227}	α	$18 \cdot 9$	days
Ra^{223}	α	$11 \cdot 2$	days
Rn^{219}	α	$3 \cdot 917$	seconds
Po^{215}	α	$1 \cdot 83 \times 10^{-3}$	seconds
Pb^{211}	β	$36 \cdot 1$	minutes
Bi^{211}	α	$2 \cdot 16$	minutes
Ti^{207}	β	$4 \cdot 76$	minutes
(finish) Pb^{207}	—	stable	

decay series can be ignored since the half-lives of the intermediate stages are so short by comparison with that of U^{235}. The series can then be simplified to:

$$U^{235} \rightarrow Pb^{207} + 7He^4 + 4 \text{ electrons}$$

Similar series have been worked out for U^{238} which decays to Pb^{206} and has a half-life of $4 \cdot 5 \times 10^9$ years and Th^{232} which produces Pb^{208} and has a half-life of $1 \cdot 39 \times 10^{10}$ years. Thus a mineral containing equal numbers of atoms of U^{238} and radiogenic Pb^{206} will be $4 \cdot 5 \times 10^9$ years old. For other proportions we can work out the age by the equation given above on page 89. The relative abundance of U^{238} to U^{235} is about 135 : 1, so that Pb^{206}/U^{238} can be determined more accurately than Pb^{207}/U^{235}. The proportion could be determined by straightforward chemical analysis, and this was the original method. Chemical analysis, however, is incapable of differentiating between the different isotopes of an element. If 'common' lead is present, which has not been produced by radioactive decay, it will be included in the total determined by chemical analysis and the age computed will be too great. Chemical analysis also cannot distinguish between the lead isotopes produced from U^{235}, U^{238} and Th ^{232}, and can only give an age based on the average of the three decay series. Thus the advance in isotope determination made possible by the mass spectrometer gave a great impetus to radiometric dating. Various refinements of method have enabled ages to be estimated with considerable accuracy by the uranium and thorium decay series.

Many radioactive minerals contain both isotopes of uranium as well as thorium, and thus three independent values for the age can be obtained by measuring the Pb^{206}/U^{238}, Pb^{207}/U^{235} and Pb^{208}/Th^{232} ratios. Ages can also be calculated from the ratio of pairs of lead isotopes, which change with time on account of the different decay constants of the parent radioactive elements. Thus it may be possible to calculate three or four ages for the same mineral. These are seldom in exact agreement. Frequently the age determined by the ratio of the lead isotopes Pb^{207} and Pb^{206} is greater than the Pb^{207}/U^{235} age, which in turn is greater than the age calculated from Pb^{206}/U^{238}.

In general, the cause of discordant ages is the loss of uranium, lead, or an intermediate member of the decay series by diffusion or by leaching. If lead has been lost, the Pb^{207}/Pb^{206} age is likely to be more reliable than the others. Thorium–lead ages are usually regarded as less reliable than uranium–lead ages.

Two other radioactive isotopes have come into use within the last few years. Rubidium^{87} decays to strontium^{87} with the emission of a β-particle for each atom decaying, but it was a long time before the half-life could be measured at all accurately. It is still uncertain and recently published figures range from $4 \cdot 7 \times 10^{10}$ to $5 \cdot 25 \times 10^{10}$ years. Ages calculated using these two extreme figures will differ by about 10 per cent. Rubidium does not form mineral species of its own and dating has been done on micas and potash felspars which contain small quantities of rubidium. Such minerals also contain common strontium, a mixture of Sr^{86}, Sr^{87} and Sr^{88}, and the isotopic composition of this must be known or assumed in order that the amount of Sr^{87} which has originated by radioactive decay can be determined. Because of the minerals in which it occurs the rubidium–strontium method has been mainly used for acid igneous, and especially for metamorphic rocks.

The decay of radioactive potassium, K^{40}, proceeds along two different paths:

$$K^{40} \nearrow \quad Ar^{40} \text{ by electron capture}$$
$$\searrow \quad Ca^{40} \text{ by } \beta \text{ emission}$$

the half-life being around $1 \cdot 26 \times 10^9$ years. The ratio between the two decay rates is known as the branching ratio. Since the K^{40} is present as a constituent of common potassium, which is a mixture of three isotopes K^{39}, K^{40} and K^{41}, the proportion of K^{40} present, known as f, must be known or assumed before ages can be calculated. There is some variation between the values of f which have been obtained. It is around $1 \cdot 18 \times 10^{-4}$ atoms of K^{40} per atom of common potassium.

In theory K^{40} offers two independent methods of age determination. In practice K^{40}/Ca^{40} is of limited application, on account of swamping of Ca^{40} by common calcium, but some successful work has been done on lepidolite and sylvite. The potassium–argon method has proved to be of greater interest. Some minerals lose argon by diffusion but it has been shown that micas, amphiboles, and pyroxenes, among others, retain it well enough. The potassium–argon method is the most versatile of radiometric methods, as regards both the kinds of rock which it can date and the range of ages which it can determine. In the case of intrusive or extrusive igneous rocks it can give a reliable figure for the emplacement of the rock. In the case of metamorphic rocks the age usually approximates to that of the latest phase of metamorphism, since metamorphism usually expels existing argon. Glauconite is known to form on the sea floor at the present time, and as it is not a very resistant mineral the glauconite in ancient sediments is usually assumed to have been formed not long before its burial, and can therefore for geological purposes be considered contemporaneous with the rock in which it occurs. Care must be taken in this case because glauconite loses argon if heated above normal atmospheric temperatures, and potassium–argon ages of glauconites are usually thought to be low, but for many sedimentary successions without intercalated igneous rocks they afford the only indications of age that we can get.

A radioactive isotope with a much shorter half-life (about 5,570 years) is carbon[14], which has proved valuable in dating late Pleistocene finds and deposits. It is considered in more detail at the end of this chapter.

THE PHANEROZOIC TIME-SCALE

I have already stressed that radiometric methods give dates for minerals and only indirectly for rocks. Ages determined by uranium and thorium methods are largely restricted to the veins in which the minerals containing these elements occur. The addition of potassium and rubidium to the list of elements useful for dating greatly increased the range of the method, for volcanic rocks and some sediments could now be dated by means of micas and glauconite respectively, and the assignment of ages in years to some of the fossiliferous rocks became a practical possibility. Volcanic rocks interbedded with sediments can often be dated using the potassium–argon method on biotite. Bentonites have been dated by various radioactive methods and may become important for assigning ages to sedimentary sequences when sufficient determinations have been made. Much of the present dating of the sedimentary succession depends, however, on ages obtained for intrusive igneous rocks. The stratigraphical gap between the youngest rocks cut by an intrusion and the oldest rocks which are known to be later than the intrusion is often wide, and the stratigraphical age of the intrusion is correspondingly doubtful.

An example of the difficulties of dating sedimentary successions is given by the Carboniferous–Permian boundary (Smith, Francis and Woodland in Harland and others 1964).

System	Stage	Radiometric dates
Permian	Sakmarian.	Sande lava, Norway, 284 m.y.
Carboniferous	Stephanian	C Castro-Daire granite, Portugal, 282±7 m.y.
		B Brassac tuffs, France, 288±8 m.y.
		A

The three ages shown are the most pertinent to the problem. The Brassac tuffs lie near the base of Stephanian B, and are well dated stratigraphically with the qualification that correlation is by means of fossil plants (p. 77). The Castro-Daire granite, which appears to afford a useful date, is less satisfactory. Its stratigraphical date depends on the assumption that it is of the same age as a petrographically similar granite which cuts sediments which are probably Stephanian B. These sediments, again, are dated by fossil plants. A conglomerate of probable lowest Permian age containing granite pebbles is regarded as later than the granite but it seems that the presence of pieces of Castro-Daire granite in the conglomerate is unproved. On this evidence the Castro-Daire granite has been dated as Stephanian C. The Sande lava is interbedded with sediments which appear to be of latest Carboniferous or early Permian age. It has been said that the biotite from the lava on which the radiometric determination was made was formed by later contact metamorphism, in which case the rock must be older than 284 million years but this is at odds with the stratigraphical dating if the other radiometric ages are reliable. The authors of the Geological Society's Symposium settled for a round figure of 280 million years for the boundary, but this clearly rests on slender evidence.

An interesting suggestion for the application of radiometric dating to a stratigraphical problem was made by F. J. Fitch and J. A. Miller (in Harland and others 1964). A major problem in British stratigraphy is the classification of the non-marine rocks called New Red Sandstone which lie between the Carboniferous and the Jurassic. South of Nottingham there are no marine intercalations at all, and although the rocks have been divided between the Permian and Triassic Systems on the dubious basis of lithology there is no good evidence as to their correlation with these systems elsewhere. Fitch and Miller noted a widespread episode of mineralization in Devon and Cornwall, also recognizable in Derbyshire, dated radiometrically to about 225 million years. This is the date provisionally assigned on independent (though not very good) evidence to the Permo–Triassic boundary elsewhere. They therefore suggested that the mineralization be taken to mark the boundary in Britain. If the mineralization can be used to distinguish between rocks deposited before it happened and those deposited after, it may be possible to recognize the boundary in local sedimentary sequences.

An example of dating of igneous rocks is provided by the granites of south-west England. There are five major plutons on land and a sixth forming Lundy Island a few miles offshore. All are emplaced in upper Palaeozoic rocks, the latest of which are Upper Carboniferous in date. The granites are therefore Permian or later, but no sediments overlie them and no upper limit of age can be set stratigraphically. The granites appear to be associated with the intense earth movements which affected the area towards the close of the Carboniferous, and were usually assumed to be of Permian age; confirmation of this was provided by the presence of heavy minerals, supposed to have been derived by erosion from the granites, in Mesozoic sedimentary rocks. Some workers made an exception for the Lundy granite, believing on petrological and geophysical grounds that it was more like the Tertiary granites of northern Britain than the other granites of south-west England. These suppositions have now been confirmed by radiometric dates: the granites of the mainland have been dated to between about 280 and 295 million years, while that of Lundy comes out at about 50 million years, and is therefore early Tertiary.

There have been many attempts to assign ages in years to the periods of the Phanerozoic and their subdivisions. In the last century these depended primarily on estimates of rates of sedimentation. Radiometric dating now provides a firm framework for the time-scale but it is still difficult to give precision to the ages of the boundaries between systems and stages. This is for two reasons: first, the radiometric ages themselves are liable to errors, and the ages available for a system may be contradictory. Second, the ages seldom apply to rocks on the boundaries and hence these have to be interpolated. This is still usually done on the assumption that the maximum thickness of a sedimentary unit is proportional to the time taken to form it. This is an unreliable guide since both experience and commonsense tell us that rates of sedimentation vary widely, but we have little choice. One of the few alternatives would be rates of evolution of fossils. These are also highly variable but within a small group of fossils might be no less reliable than rates of sedimentation.

The latest attempt to compile a scale resulted from a symposium held in 1964 by the Geological Societies of London and Glasgow (Harland and others 1964). The main features of the scale (Fig. 15) are unlikely to be altered much by future work, but it will be a long time before radiometric dating is able to help much with purely stratigraphical problems in the Phanerozoic.

PRE-CAMBRIAN STRATIGRAPHY

Radiometric dating has shown that Pre-Cambrian rocks account for at least four-fifths of geological time as recorded in the

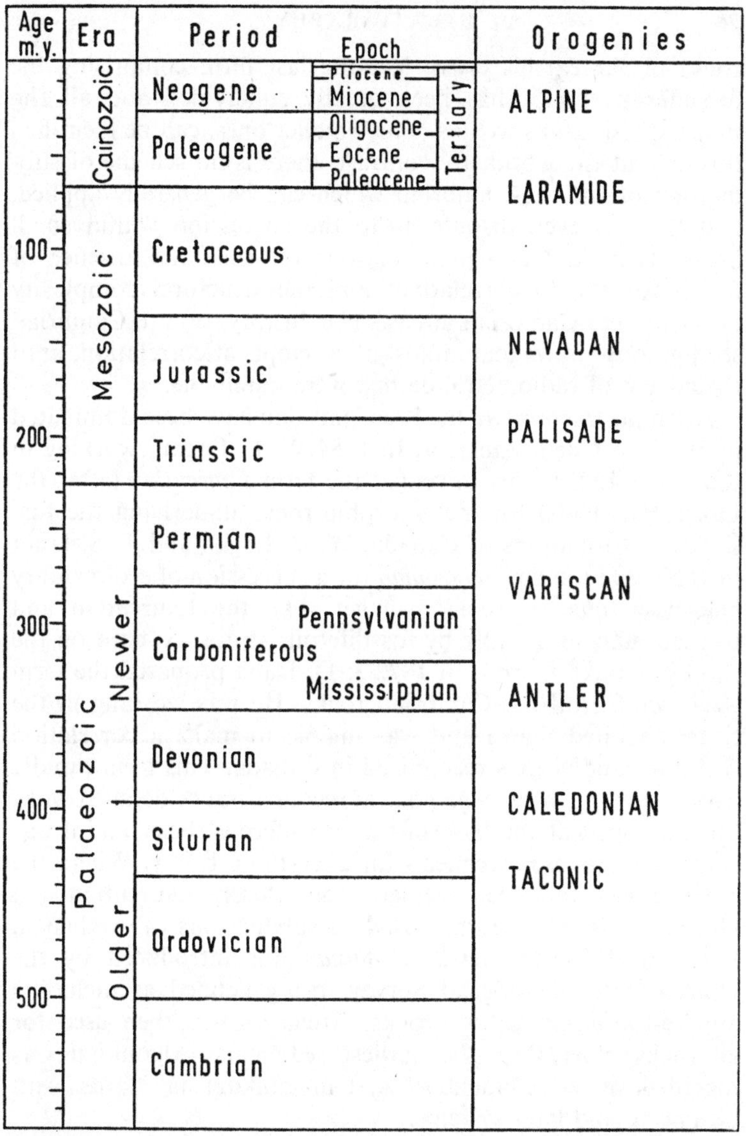

Age m.y.	Era	Period	Epoch		Orogenies
	Cainozoic	Neogene	Pliocene / Miocene	Tertiary	ALPINE
		Paleogene	Oligocene / Eocene / Paleocene		
100	Mesozoic	Cretaceous			LARAMIDE
		Jurassic			NEVADAN
200		Triassic			PALISADE
	Palaeozoic Newer	Permian			VARISCAN
300		Carboniferous	Pennsylvanian		
			Mississippian		ANTLER
		Devonian			
400	Palaeozoic Older	Silurian			CALEDONIAN
					TACONIC
		Ordovician			
500		Cambrian			

FIG. 15. The Phanerozoic eras and periods with Cainozoic epochs. Ages in millions of years (m.y.) from Harland and others (1964). The ages of all boundaries are subject to uncertainty, which in some cases may amount to ± 10 m.y. The small space above the Pliocene represents the Quaternary (Pleistocene and Holocene Epochs). Some well-known orogenies in Europe and North America are shown in the right-hand column.

G

rocks of the earth's crust. Yet the last fifth, comprising the fossiliferous rocks, has been greatly subdivided and all the major divisions, as well as many smaller ones, can be identified throughout the world. By contrast, there is no scheme of sub-division of the Pre-Cambrian which can be generally applied, and there is even dispute as to the succession within small areas. There are two main reasons for this: the absence of fossils for use in correlation, and the structural complexity of many Pre-Cambrian areas. The history of Pre-Cambrian stratigraphy shows that almost all attempts at correlation, until the advent of radiometric dating, were unreliable.

Attempts to correlate the Pre-Cambrian have been dominated by work in North America. In 1854 W. E. Logan, working in the Great Lakes area, invented the term *Laurentian* (after the Laurentian Hills) for metamorphic rocks underlying the fos-siliferous formations of Canada. W. E. Logan and T. S. Hunt in 1855 used the term *Huronian* for a succession of sedimentary and basic igneous rocks younger than the Laurentian and overlain unconformably by fossiliferous strata, exposed on the shores of Lake Huron. In 1872 J. D. Dana proposed the term *Archaean* for all Pre-Cambrian rocks. He was working in the eastern United States and was unable to make a correlation with the subdivisions recognized in Canada. This term rapidly gained favour. In early geological reconnaissance detailed work often stopped at the base of the fossiliferous rocks, and it was convenient to use Archaean for everything below. Where the oldest rocks had been studied more closely Laurentian and Huronian were sometimes used as subdivisions of Archaean. Later, in 1889, the term *Algonkian* was introduced by the United States Geological Survey, being defined as including all Pre-Cambrian Clastic rocks. Archaean was then used for all rocks older than the earliest sediments. Algonkian was regarded as a sedimentary system ranking in status with Cambrian and later systems.

Time-terms for the Pre-Cambrian were invented towards the end of the century. *Proterozoic* was suggested by S. F. Emmons in 1888 as a time-term equivalent to Algonkian. *Archaeozoic* was introduced by J. D. Dana in 1872, and defined on a theoretical basis: its beginning coincided with the appearance of the earliest living organisms. This is not, of course, a practical criterion. Nevertheless the term was soon adopted as a time equivalent to Archaean.

In 1905 a fourfold subdivision was proposed for the Pre-Cambrian of the Lake Superior region (Adams and others 1905):

Keweenawan (Nipigon)

~~~~~~~~~~~~~~~~~~~~~~~ unconformity

Huronian (Lower, Middle and Upper, separated by unconformities)

~~~~~~~~~~~~~~~~~~~~~~~ unconformity

Keewatin

——————————————— eruptive contact

Laurentian

These names were applied to rock groups. All are more or less metamorphosed. The Laurentian consisted of granites, the Keewatin of a thick succession of lavas with some interbedded sediments. The Huronian is an extensive sedimentary accumulation and the Keweenawan consists of sediments with some igneous rocks. This classification acquired wide currency because it was adopted by T. C. Chamberlin and R. D. Salisbury in their *Textbook of Geology* (1904–1906) in the following form:

| Algonkian or Proterozoic | { | Keweenawan Huronian |
| Archaeozoic or Archaean | { | Keewatin Laurentian |

In 1907 C. R. Van Hise in a presidential address to the Geological Society of America applied this scheme on a world-wide scale, purporting to recognize the equivalents of the North American rocks in other continents (Van Hise 1908). Now in any region, if the crust is probed deeply enough, stratified rocks are eventually found to rest on metamorphic rocks, and the term Archaean came to be applied to this crystalline basement in many countries. As a purely descriptive term for the earliest known rocks of an area it is possibly useful. It was often taken, however, to imply correlation, all Archaean rocks being assumed to have been the result of the same metamorphic episode. There is no justification for this assumption, but in extenuation it must be remembered that the immensity of Pre-Cambrian time was not generally appreciated, and for long the hypothesis of a single Pre-Cambrian orogeny may have seemed plausible.

In the 'Proterozoic' red sediments are found in a number of regions, for example in the Keweenawan of North America, the Torridonian of Scotland and the Jotnian or Sparagmitan in Scandinavia. These again were correlated, but with no more reason than any other barren, lithologically similar formations, such as the Old Red Sandstone and New Red Sandstone of Britain, might be equated.

A warning against the absurdity of these lithological correlations had already been sounded, had it been heeded. A stir was caused by H. Reusch (1883) when he reported Silurian fossils in rocks which had been originally classified as 'Archaean' in Norway, and J. J. Sederholm in Finland in 1899 found crystalline rocks to pass laterally into sediments. Sir Archibald Geikie in 1893 compiled a list of schists which included representatives of most of the geological systems, to emphasize the absurdity of dating a rock by its lithology or regarding metamorphic rocks as necessarily Pre-Cambrian. Nevertheless, attempts to establish lithological correlations between widely-separated areas of Pre-Cambrian rocks continued until quite recent times.

Returning to Canada, J. E. Gill (1955) has maintained that many of the classical names have been so often used wrongly that terms such as Huronian, Laurentian and so on should be restricted to their original meanings to denote local rock groups in their type localities, although some of them are not even satisfactorily defined for this limited purpose (Thomson 1953). Gill rejects the division into Archaean and Proterozoic and uses expressions such as 'Early Pre-Cambrian' and 'Late Pre-Cambrian' when time terms are needed. I note later (p. 150) that 'system' (a biostratigraphical term, see p. 149) is still used for rock groups in the Pre-Cambrian, but clearly these systems are lithostratigraphical units of local validity. It may be better to drop 'system' and substitute some other term. It is too early to say what nomenclature will emerge as a result of the correlations by radiometric dating now being carried on; there is force to the argument that it should be of a different kind, using different units, from that which was worked out to suit the fossiliferous rocks.

Radiometric methods are now revolutionizing Pre-Cambrian stratigraphy and with improved techniques and more and more determinations the main Pre-Cambrian orogenies will doubtless be securely dated and correlated. The Svecofennian–Karelide metamorphism in Finland has been recognized in Sweden and has been claimed to correspond with the episodes known as Hudsonian in Canada and Penokean in the United States, all at around 1,800 million years ago. The episode called Sveconorwegian in Scandinavia appears to correspond in age with the Grenville orogeny in North America, about 950 million years ago (Magnusson 1965). At present, however, ages obtained for the main episodes in different areas do not always correspond, and it would be unjustifiable to attempt to force the evidence to fit a world-wide pattern. Study of Cambrian and later rocks gives no reason to believe that orogenies are world-wide in their effects, or that the most intense phases of a particular orogeny are synchronous everywhere. Any hope of recognizing certain episodes throughout the Pre-Cambrian areas of the world is probably better abandoned. We may legitimately hope to recognize each episode whenever it may occur and thus to work out the geographical extent of the Pre-Cambrian orogenies. Ultimately we may be able to reconstruct something of the conditions on the earth's surface during Pre-Cambrian time.

For a long time such Pre-Cambrian fossils as had been described were the subjects of controversy and some of them are now believed to be of inorganic origin. More recently convincing fossils have been described from the later Pre-Cambrian, for example of Charnwood Forest, Leicestershire in England and the Ediacara Hills in South Australia. Several animal phyla are represented including coelenterates, segmented worms and flatworms, and unidentified, possibly extinct groups. Although further finds may be expected there is little hope that zoning by fossils, in the usual sense, will become practicable. Fossil localities and horizons are rare, and in addition the fossils are likely to have belonged to slowly-evolving groups. More common fossils are algae and Russian stratigraphers maintain that stromatolites (structures built by calcareous algae) can be successfully used to define biostratigraphical subdivisions in the late Pre-Cambrian sediments of

Eastern Siberia (Koroljuk 1960). The Pre-Cambrian stromato-lites have been divided into about 30 form-species. In sequences totalling some thousands of metres the Russians have recognized three successive assemblages of these between about 1,600 million years ago and the base of the Cambrian. The criticism has been made that some of the form-species depend on the environment on which they lived, but Koroljuk states that identical groups of stromatolites have been found in different facies. If the value of stromatolites is confirmed they may provide a means of biostratigraphical correlation within the later Pre-Cambrian rocks; even so, the units which can be defined will be very large by comparison with those in later rocks.

Although world-wide correlation of Pre-Cambrian rocks can now be attempted, the precision with which it can be done, even under the most favourable circumstances, is far from that of biostratigraphical correlation in the Phanerozoic systems. Few radiometric ages for the Pre-Cambrian have probable errors smaller than ± 25 million years, compared with less than 1 million years for the best zonal schemes (p. 71). With present methods the best Pre-Cambrian correlation is likely to be 50 to 100 times less accurate than the best correlation in fossili-ferous rocks.

RADIOCARBON DATING

The radioactive isotope carbon[14] decays to stable nitrogen[14] with the emission of one β-particle for each atom of carbon. The half-life of C^{14} is about 5,570 years, and the isotope would have long since virtually disappeared from the earth if it were not being continually produced in the upper atmosphere by the bombardment of nitrogen[14] atoms by cosmic rays. There is a balance between production and decay and the amount of C^{14} in the atmosphere remains constant within narrow limits. It is taken up along with ordinary carbon from the atmosphere by plants and through them by animals, and therefore the pro-portion of C^{14} present in living animals and plants is also reasonably constant. This proportion is, however, very small, only about one part in one billion (10^{12}) of the total carbon present. Radiocarbon dating rests on the assumption that this proportion has been constant for the last 50,000 years or so. This is not strictly true because there has been a decrease in the C^{14} content of the atmosphere since the industrial revolution due to dilution by the inert carbon isotope C^{12} in carbon dioxide from the combustion of fuels, such as coal, whose carbon[14] has long since vanished. An estimate can be made of the pre-industrial value.

As soon as an animal or plant dies its carbon[14] is no longer replenished, and the amount is reduced by one-half every 5,570 years. The length of time which has elapsed since the death of an organism can be found by measuring the proportion of carbon[14] left. In theory this is easily done. The carbon[14] emits β-particles at a known rate as it decays and the amount of carbon[14] can be found by counting the rate of β-particle emission by a known mass of carbon. There are various standard ways of doing this, such as geiger tubes, scintillation counters and exposure to photographic plates. Practical difficulties arise from the very small proportion of carbon[14] present. For samples of appreciable age the rate of β-particle emission is comparable with β-activity in the atmosphere, and many technical refinements have been tried to reduce interference by background activity, including various types of shield and anti-coincidence circuits, while another approach involves artificially increasing the concentration of carbon[14] before counting. As with other methods of radiometric dating, the instrumental refinements and technical skill necessary for successful dating are only to be found in a few laboratories which have specialized in the method. Dates can now be obtained back to 40,000 or 50,000 years ago, and one or two skilled workers have determined ages up to about 70,000 years. There does not seem to be much prospect of this range being substantially increased, and some workers regard about 20,000 years as being the limit of reliable ages.

The radiocarbon method is useful for correlation only in the latest part of geological time, but it is precisely here that we want to make very fine stratigraphical subdivision on account of the interest in the later developments of human culture and in the evolution of our own environment. Most of the rocks concerned are of very limited extent—cave deposits, peats, and so on—so that the sequence cannot be established by super-

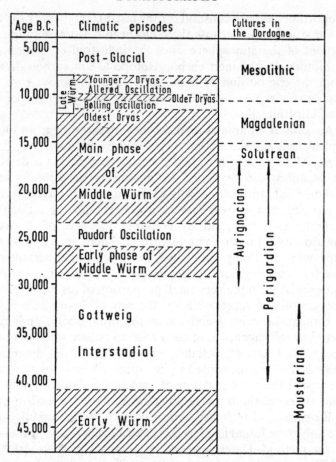

FIG. 16. Subdivisions of the Last (Würm) Glaciation, and ranges of some European stone age cultures. Cold periods shaded. Ages in years based on radiocarbon dates. After Movius (1960).

position, and normal methods of correlation are largely inapplicable. Many of the deposits contain organic material such as wood or bones, and with proper selection of material to minimize loss of carbon by leaching, reliable ages can often be obtained. Late Pleistocene stratigraphy has been greatly improved since about 1950 by the use of the method. Much progress has certainly been made since the 1939–1945 war by other methods, but local sections are still largely characterized

climatically, by inference from the faunal and physical characters of sediments, and correlation between them is achieved by
matching up climatic sequences. This has obvious dangers
because similar climatic sequences may not be of the same age.
Radiocarbon dating has reinforced the climatic method and
has enabled many isolated sites to be fitted into the general
scheme. A simple version of the Last Glaciation with the ranges
of certain archaeological cultures is shown in Figure 16.

5

LITHOLOGICAL VARIATION
AND FACIES

LITHOLOGICAL variation concerns the stratigrapher in two ways. On the one hand, he must devise methods of recording it, and on the other, he must find out the relationship of the lithological changes to time. The second activity involves the processes of correlation already described in Chapters 2 and 3. The description of variable lithology naturally makes great use of maps and diagrams, since words are less precise. The simplest device is the longitudinal section. Sections drawn to illustrate variations in lithology and thickness are often drawn with the vertical scale many times greater than the horizontal so that the succession may be shown in sufficient detail. Tectonics are usually ignored, and instead a suitable stratigraphical datum level is drawn as a horizontal line. Geological literature abounds with examples. If there are considerable thickness variations the section will show spurious 'dips' and it must be remembered that these bear no relationship to actual dips. On account of this there is a limit to the thickness of beds which can be conveniently shown in a section and it is usually preferable to have several sections for successive units rather than one very thick one. In Figure 23 the highest coal seam has been arbitrarily drawn as horizontal. If the Upper Cwmgorse Marine Band had been made horizontal the beds would appear to dip the other way. Such a diagram can be drawn as a result of lithological mapping without any reference to processes of zoning or correlation, as exemplified by Figures 17 and 22.

In another kind of diagram zonal boundaries (or other isochronous surfaces) are drawn as horizontal lines (Figs 13, 18, 20B). Such diagrams indicate correlation but cannot show thickness variations, since the vertical scale of the diagram is time and not thickness. Figure 20 contrasts diagrams for the Inferior

Oolite of part of southern England with the vertical scale (A) thickness and (B) time. Alternatively isochronous lines may be drawn on a section, as in Figure 24B, and in this case correlation and thickness variations may be shown in the same diagram.

Where fossil zones or other reliable time markers are available it is often seen, as in Figures 18, 23 and 24, that lithological boundaries vary in age from place to place. In such cases two sets of names are used: formation or lithostratigraphical names to describe the lithological units, and zonal or biostratigraphical names to describe subdivisions based on fossils, which one hopes will approximate to time divisions. Usually the distinction between them will be obvious, as the biostratigraphical names will normally be combined with the word 'zone', 'stage', etc. Although this dual classification is well established and generally accepted, there is no uniformity of procedure. The Permian of south-eastern New Mexico furnishes an instructive case. Limestone in the south-east passes laterally into red beds and evaporites in the north-west. The US Geological Survey, mapping the area, named the limestone the Carlsbad Limestone and the red beds the Chalk Bluff Formation, and as the two were found to interfinger names were also given to the principal tongues (Fig. 18a). Each name thus identifies the facies of the unit and its approximate position, but precise correlation is not expressed. Petroleum geologists worked out a different classification shown in Figure 18b. According to King (1949) who drew attention to this case, this 'gives precisely the age of the beds. It can be mapped on the surface, but only by the painstaking tracing of marker beds'. The formation boundaries in this case, therefore, are believed to be time lines. The need for this kind of classification is clear: it enables us to make 'precise determinations of structure' and to say, for example, to what part of the Carlsbad Limestone a given part of the red beds corresponds. It is misleading, however, to call the units in it formations, for rock units and units defined by supposed time-planes are thus given the same name and the fundamental distinction between them is hidden.

Lateral variation in thickness of a unit may be shown by means of an isopach map. Such maps may be compiled from outcrop data (in well-dissected country), borehole logs or a

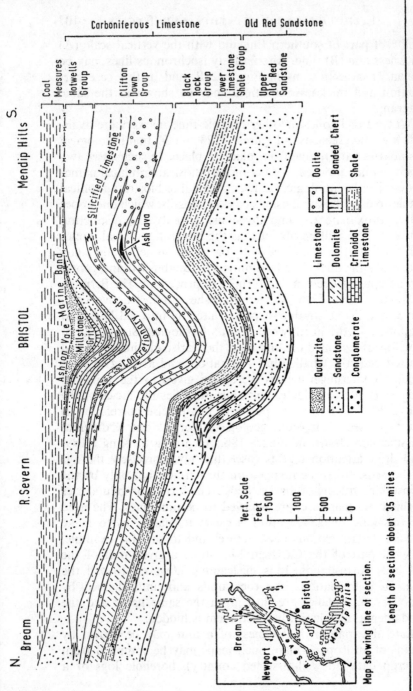

Fig. 17. Thickness and facies changes in the Upper Old Red Sandstone, Carboniferous Limestone and Millstone Grit between the Forest of Dean (Glos.) and Mendip Hills (Som.), England. The Carboniferous Limestone is divided lithologically into four groups which may be diachronous; no isochronous horizons are available to determine this. The diagram has been constructed by taking a level near the base of the Coal Measures as a straight line and plotting thicknesses below it, resulting in an apparent 'syncline' at Bristol due to the presence there

combination of both. Some degree of generalization is naturally involved, and will depend on the number of points at which thickness is known. An isopach map may be a convenient way of defining a small unit, such as a member or lens of restricted lateral extent. Isopach maps of large stratigraphical units such as systems or their major subdivisions often reflect the form and extent of original depositional basins. The development of basins has been studied in particular by petroleum geologists. Characteristically the most complete succession is found where the rocks are thickest, while non-sequences and unconformities (Chapter 6) develop as the sequence is traced to the margins of the basin.

Many lithostratigraphical units get thinner or wedge out

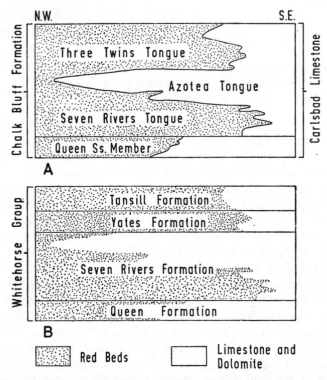

FIG. 18. Alternative classifications of part of the Permian Guadelupe Series in south-eastern New Mexico, U.S.A. In B horizontal lines are formation boundaries. From King (1949).

towards the margins of a basin or towards a 'swell' or less strongly downwarped area. Thinning may occur in several ways which can be examined if suitable fossil zones are present. First, the whole unit may thin uniformly, individual zones being reduced in proportion. Secondly, non-sequences may develop, or zones may be represented by condensed beds. In part of the Toarcian Stage of Alsace shown in Figure 19

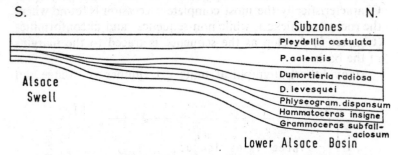

FIG. 19. Thinning and wedging out of the ammonite subzones of the upper part of the Toarcian Stage in the Jurassic of Alsace, France. Length of section about 50 miles. Vertical scale greatly exaggerated. After Schirardin (1961).

only four of seven subzones present in the basin persist over the Alsace swell, and three of these get thinner. Thirdly, if the unit is transgressive the base will be progressively younger from the centre towards the margin of the basin, higher zones overlapping lower. This is shown by the successive zones of the Lutetian Calcaire grossier in the Paris Basin (Fig. 28). Fourthly, if deposition of the unit was followed by erosion, this is most likely to affect the shallow-water marginal areas, so that higher zones are removed in this area. This is shown by the Lower and Middle Inferior Oolite between Bath and Cheltenham (Fig. 20) where successively higher zones have a smaller geographical extent because they were partly removed by erosion before the Upper Inferior Oolite was laid down. Many formations do not have good enough fossil zoning to show what actually happens, but we may suspect that one or more of the four factors mentioned above is operating. The third and fourth will produce formations with diachronous boundaries.

FACIES

The word *facies* refers to all the characters of a sedimentary unit, both lithological and palaeontological. The idea of a particular environment of origin is often, though not always, involved. Thus we may speak of deltaic facies, or turbidite facies, but also of graptolitic facies, limestone facies, and so on, when the mode of origin is not explicit and may be disputed. A facies term describes in one or two words a complex set of characters and the complex group of factors which have given rise to them, and is thus a convenient shorthand in the fields of stratigraphy and sedimentology. The scope of the term may be broad or narrow. Expressions such as 'marine facies' and 'continental facies' are in common use, and so are much more specific ones such as coral-reef facies and delta-front facies. In all these cases, however, a particular environment is referred to, whether this is broadly defined, and capable of further subdivision, or narrowly specified. The use of a particular facies term for certain rocks at once implies a certain degree of similarity with other rocks which have some characters in common, and were laid down under broadly similar conditions.

The word is used in a variety of ways and there is no need to restrict it to any one usage. Thus we may refer to the 'graptolitic facies of the Ordovician', meaning all the formations which are characterized by this facies, or the 'littoral facies of the —— formation' if we do not wish to differentiate the part formed under near-shore conditions as a separate formation. We may say that a formation or other unit is in such-and-such a facies. It follows that facies is a generic or descriptive term, and should not, in general, be used as part of the proper names of stratigraphical units.

In the past, as at present, there existed side by side a great variety of depositional environments both in the sea and on land, which gave rise to different facies of the same age. This has two principal consequences for stratigraphy. First, palaeontological correlation between different facies is often difficult, since different environments have different faunas. Second, there is often a strong similarity between facies of like origin but of different ages, so that they may be erroneously correlated.

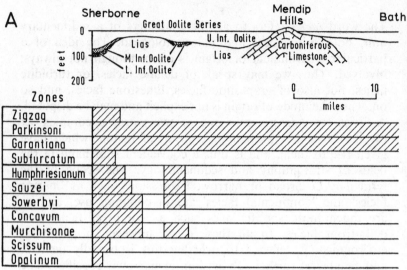

It is a commonplace of geology that the correlation of rocks in different facies often presents difficulties. These vary greatly in degree, and tend to be less with correlations which depend on pelagic fossils than with those depending on benthonic fossils. In the Mesozoic the ammonoids are found in a great variety of marine facies and permit correlation between them; the difficulties which do arise do so mainly because of the existence at certain times of faunal provinces (p. 63). Even so there are facies in which ammonoids are very rare, such as the oolitic and coralline facies in the Jurassic and much of the European chalk. By contrast, the graptolites in the Ordovician and Silurian are largely restricted to sediments of a certain type, in this case dark mudstones and shales. These restrictions of pelagic organisms to facies may be due to unfavourable conditions for fossilization rather than to original distribution: the fragile shells of ammonites may have been easily broken up in the current-swept waters in which oolites were deposited, and the delicate graptolites may not have survived the disturbed waters in which the shelly facies was laid down.

Many benthonic organisms are restricted to certain habitats and so are restricted to certain sedimentary facies when they become fossilized. Such species are often known as *facies*

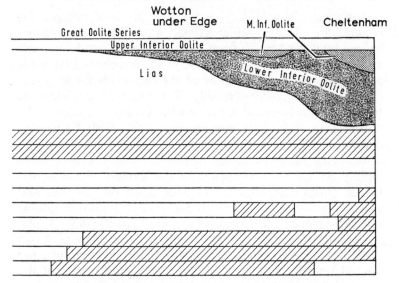

FIG. 20. The Inferior Oolite (Jurassic) of part of southern England.
A, distribution and thickness variation of the three major lithostratigraphical subdivisions. The top of the Upper Inferior Oolite
has been drawn as a horizontal line. B, distribution of the ammonite
zones. Based in part on Kellaway and Welch (1948).

fossils. For example, in the seas around Britain at the present
day different species of heart-urchin live in sediments of different grain-size, *Echinocardium cordatum* being found in clean
sand and *Spatangus purpureus* in shell gravel, while *S. raschi*
lives in sandy mud. It is easy to see how burrowing animals,
such as heart-urchins and some lamellibranchs, may be
restricted to certain sediment types since their feeding mechan-
isms and other vital processes may be adapted to a particular
range of particle sizes.

Other animals may be restricted to certain depth ranges.
The example of the reef corals is well known. They are limited
to a maximum depth of about 150 feet by the requirement of
light for their symbiotic green algae (zooxanthellae) to photo-
synthesize. They are also limited to a water temperature of
over 15°C. Many other examples of species, animal-types or
whole communities restricted to certain habitats may be found
in ecological literature.

H

Benthonic animals may sometimes have advantages for stratigraphy. T. G. Miller (1965) has distinguished zones defined by pelagic fossils from those defined by benthonic ones as *p*-zones and *b*-zones respectively. He maintains that while *p*-zones are the more valuable of the two kinds for long distance correlation, *b*-zones usually allow greater local refinement. Insofar as this is true it is presumably because changes in the composition of the bottom fauna may occur fairly frequently, due to local changes of circumstances, or perhaps because in some cases small benthonic populations may evolve fairly rapidly. Miller gives examples: in the Caradoc Series of the British Ordovician, fourteen *b*-zones based on trilobites and brachiopods correspond to two and part of a third graptolite zones (*p*-zones). In the English Cornbrash Arkell (1933, p. 326) accepts four brachiopod zones (*b*-zones) corresponding to two ammonite zones (*p*-zones). It is questionable, however, whether this relationship is a general rule. Throughout much of the Mesozoic benthonic faunas certainly changed more slowly than the ammonoid faunas. The coral-brachiopod zones of the British Lower Carboniferous (p. 41) provide another example where benthonic faunas afford relatively coarse subdivision only.

The presence of facies-fossils is obvious in many successions where certain associations are restricted to certain rock-types. They are often obstacles to correlation and sometimes constitute a positive danger. Correlation between different facies, if zonal fossils independent of the facies are absent, must often remain approximate or doubtful. The danger arises when a facies fossil is associated with a rock-type which is of different ages at different places, and when the fossil is believed to be a time-indicator so that the occurrences of different ages are correlated For instance older zonal tables for the British Upper Cretaceous included at the base a zone of *Pecten asper*. Later work suggested that this was a facies fossil restricted to the Upper Greensand facies, which is shown by other fossils and by the dating of beds above and below to be older in the south-east and younger in the west and north of Britain.

More rarely, a sequence of zones may be simulated by facies change. Oil wells in the Los Angeles and Ventura basins in California have penetrated between 10,000 and 15,000 feet of beds of presumed Pliocene age which can be divided into a number of foraminiferal zones. The zones occur in the same order, and are of comparable thickness, in both basins which are not far apart. Although the zones are not founded on evolutionary sequences (most of the species are still living) it might be thought that correlation between the basins is certain. Study of the distribution of Foraminifera on the floor of the adjacent Pacific shows that this need not be so. The foraminiferal assemblages of the sedimentary basins are also found on the modern sea floor. Each assemblage has a well-defined depth range, and the order in which they occur, from deep to shallow water, is the same as that of the zonal assemblages from the lower to the higher strata. It is clear that the sequence of zones could have arisen by sedimentation starting in deep water which became steadily shallower as the basins silted up. The sequences in the two basins are homotaxial (see p. 30) but it is not certain that corresponding zones are synchronous because there is no evidence that the two basins happened to be of the same depth at the same time (Woodford 1963).

Correlation of similar facies of different ages is a mistake especially likely to be made in the early stages of geological investigation of an area, and it is usually rectified when detailed fossil collecting has been done. Conversely, lateral facies change within beds of the same age has often led to the different facies being thought to be of different ages. This may have happened with the Silurian rocks of Gotland, described later in this chapter. Permian clastic rocks in the Ural mountains pass westwards into limestones which contain a different fossil fauna and were long believed to be of Carboniferous age, giving rise to the Upper Carboniferous stage-name Uralian proposed by A. A. de Lapparent in 1893. Similarly d'Orbigny's Urgonian substage was based on reef limestones which were thought to characterize a particular part of the Lower Cretaceous succession. These limestones were later found to be lateral equivalents of rocks in ammonitiferous facies which had given rise to the stage-name Barremian, and Urgonian was then abandoned.

Lateral and vertical facies change gives rise to great inequalities in degree of subdivision, and this is one reason why it is desirable that stratigraphical nomenclature should not be too rigid. In the southern English Upper Jurassic the Corallian Beds, about 300 feet thick, are divided into ten lithological subdivisions while the Oxford Clay (600 feet) below and Kimmeridge Clay (1,800 feet) above are not subdivided on lithology at all. The Corallian Beds in places pass laterally into the Ampthill Clay which is not subdivided either. The advantage of a flexible system is that it allows local subdivision to be made as fine as desired without multiplying the number of formal categories. The question is discussed further in Chapter 7.

REEF FACIES AND THE SILURIAN STRATIGRAPHY OF GOTLAND

The Silurian rocks of the Swedish island of Gotland in the Baltic offer an interesting example of a succession which can be interpreted in different ways according to the way in which the facies present are understood. The geological map shows a number of formations which lie in fairly regular outcrops across the island striking from north-east to south-west. They comprise mainly limestones and marls with a few small areas of sandstone. They yield abundant fossils which indicate a range in age from late Llandovery to Ludlow. The rocks are well-exposed on the coast but intermittently exposed inland, so that relationships between the formations cannot always be established by direct observation. The oldest rock is the Lower Visby Marl which is exposed along the north-west coast, and earlier geologists inferred a general south-easterly dip and concluded that the other formations followed in regular superposition, each overlying the one which lay to the north-west of it. Dips in various directions (presumably depositional) are observed near the numerous reef limestones, while elsewhere the rocks appear to be nearly horizontal. J. E. Hede (1921) gave the following succession:

Sundre Limestone (reef and crinoidal limestones), 10 m
Hamra Limestone (marly and crinoidal limestones with reefs), 40 m
Burgsvik Sandstone and Oolite, 50 m
Eke Group (marly and crinoidal limestones, reefs), 15 m
Hemse Group (marly and crinoidal limestones, reefs), 100 m
Klinteberg Limestone (crinoidal, detrital and oolitic limestones, with
    reefs), 100 m

Mulde Marl, 25 m
Halla Limestone (reef limestones, oolitic and detrital limestones), 15 m
Slite Group (clays, marls, marly and oolitic limestones, reefs), 100 m
Tofta Limestone (bedded limestones), 10 m
Högklint Limestone (reef and detrital limestones), 20 m
Upper Visby Marl, 10 m
Lower Visby Marl, 10 m

The total thickness obtained by adding the individual thicknesses is 505 m. The presence of reefs in most of the limestone formations will be noted, and Hede's interpretation admits of a good deal of facies change within the formations; for example, the Eke Group and the Hemse Group each tend to change from reefs with accompanying detrital limestones in the north-east to marly beds in the south-west. Both coral and stromatoporoid reefs are present. The detrital limestones often include crinoidal limestones and are generally of organic origin. The clastic material was thought to have been chiefly brought in from the north-west.

A re-interpretation involving facies change and lateral equivalence of formations on a much grander scale has been proposed by Ulrich Jux (1957). He recognized three reef-complexes which he named the Visby Group, Klinteberg Group and Burgsvik Group. These correspond to Hede's subdivisions roughly as follows:

Jux		*Hede*
Burgsvik Group	{	Burgsvik Sandstone and Oolite, Hamra Limestone, Sundre Limestone.
Klinteberg Group	{	Halla Limestone, Mulde Marl, Klinteberg Limestone, Hemse Group, Eke Group.
Visby Group	{	L. and U. Visby Marls, Högklint Limestone, Tofta Limestone, Slite Group

Within each formation, however, Hede's subdivisions do not (according to Jux) occur in sequence. Jux interprets the Gotland reefs as being flanked by facies belts (Fig. 21) which at the time of greatest extent of the reef were roughly as follows, from north-west to south-east: (land) sandstone—oolite—algal limestone—lagoonal marls—reef detritus limestone—reef—reef detritus limestone—marl and clay (open sea). Of course the facies interfinger and show irregular boundaries in plan. In the Klinteberg Group the near-shore sandstone and oolite facies is represented by the Halla Limestone; the outcrop of this formation wedges out south-westwards, and is replaced by Mulde Marl, interpreted as a lagoonal deposit. The reef itself with accompanying detrital limestones is the Klinteberg Limestone; the Hemse and Eke Groups include some detrital limestones but are largely marls representing the more fine-grained facies seaward of the reef.

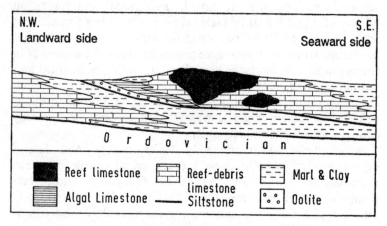

FIG. 21. Relationships of facies in the Silurian rocks of Gotland, Sweden. Length of section about 30 miles. Vertical scale greatly exaggerated. Based on Jux (1957).

The three main groups occur in sequence—this is shown by graptolites from the marls—but within each group the formations of Hede are believed to be lateral equivalents. The fossils other than graptolites are facies-fossils of little value for correlation.

By following the methods used by William Smith (p. 16) Hede established a succession of thirteen successive formations which, according to Jux, is spurious. Smith was lucky in that the formations he mapped in south-west England show little facies change and most of them are not strongly diachronous. Hede was less fortunate in applying the same principles to an area of reef-dominated sedimentation with its numerous laterally-equivalent facies.

What of Hede's stratigraphical names? If they prove useful they may presumably be retained, although some adjustment might be desirable to make them correspond more closely with the facies.

DIACHRONISM

I have already remarked that in cases where suitable zoning is available, the boundaries of formations (defined primarily on lithology) are often found to be of variable age. The term *diachronous* was invented for such beds by W. B. Wright in 1926. It is likely that many other formations, for which precise dating is not possible, are also diachronous, and indeed that diachronism is the rule, not the exception, for formations. If it were not so, stratigraphers would not be so reluctant to correlate on the basis of rock-type, and lithological correlations would not be so often found to be wrong.

Diachronism may arise in various ways. It will occur if the base of a formation is transgressive, or if the upper part has been affected locally by non-deposition or erosion in areas of shallow water (p. 110). It may be caused by the lateral shifting of facies boundaries as deposition proceeds. In the Devonian of New York State, referred to below, the boundary between the marine and the red beds facies shifted steadily westwards with time, so that the red beds (Catskill Group or facies) have a diachronous lower boundary. In the Carboniferous Limestone of Gloucestershire and Somerset (Fig. 17) oolites accumulated during a longer period in the south than in the north, but zoning is not good enough to reveal detailed relationships. A section such as this suggests a constantly changing pattern of facies, but as we cannot draw closely-spaced isochronous lines on the section the changes cannot be followed in detail.

In the Great Oolite of the southern Cotswolds, shown in Figure 22, there is at present no means of correlating the lithological units which have been established by mapping, but in view of the rapid lateral variation it is unlikely that many of the boundaries are isochronous. In this particular instance lithological correlations were made before the com-

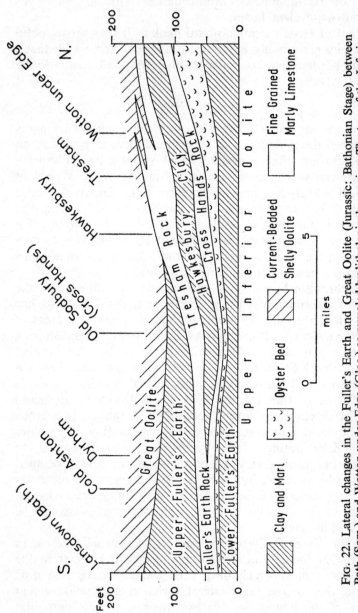

FIG. 22. Lateral changes in the Fuller's Earth and Great Oolite (Jurassic: Bathonian Stage) between Bath (Som.) and Wotton-under-Edge (Glos.) as revealed by lithological mapping. The top of the Inferior Oolite has been drawn as a horizontal line. No isochronous horizons have been found. Modified from Arkell and Donovan (1952).

plexity of the case was realized. At Lansdown the Inferior Oolite and Great Oolite are separated by Fuller's Earth clays with an intermediate band of rock, the Fuller's Earth Rock. About seventeen miles to the north, around Wotton-under-Edge, a similar lithological succession was observed which has similar topographic expression, the oolite at the top forming the hill summits. The two successions almost identical and lithological correlation was plausible until mapping revealed the state of affairs shown in Figure 22. The Cross Hands Rock of Wotton has originated by the splitting of the rock at Lansdown, and neither the upper clay nor the upper oolite is continuous between the two places; both are new formations.

A case in which variation in age can be proved is afforded by the Pennant Sandstone of South Wales. In the early days of geological study in the South Wales, Bristol and Somerset Coalfields a conspicuous and easily mappable group of massive felspathic sandstones was recognized within the Coal Measures, and named Pennant Grit from a local quarrymen's term. The Pennant Series for long served to divide the Lower Coal Series from the Upper Coal Series, and these three divisions of the Coal Measures were shown on the geological maps. It was believed for a while that lower and upper limits of the Pennant sandstones were each of constant age, being defined by particular coal seams which may be regarded as isochronous surfaces (see p. 79). In recent years the Geological Survey of Great Britain has shown that the earlier correlations between seams in different areas were wrong and that in fact sandstone deposition began at different times in different places (Fig. 23). As a consequence of this discovery the Survey abandoned the term Pennant Series as defined by the development of the Pennant sandstones and proposed to recognize a new unit called Pennant Measures, defined by a marine band (at the base) and by coal seams and therefore having isochronous boundaries. The term is, strictly speaking, unnecessary because it is synonymous with Upper Coal Measures as currently used in a biostratigraphical sense by the Survey (p. 155). However, it was stated that

'One feature that distinguishes the Upper Coal Measures of the South Wales Coalfield and its neighbours from the same

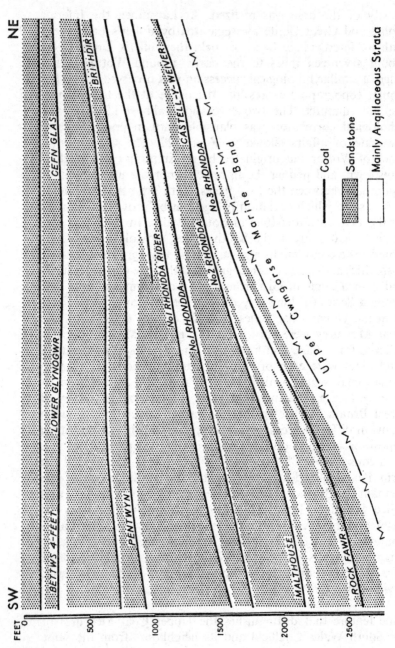

FIG. 23. Generalized section across the South Wales Coalfield showing the passage of the lower part of the Pennant Sandstone (stippled) into shales towards the north-east. The marine band and coal seams are believed

formation elsewhere, is the large-scale development of felds-
pathic sandstone and grit of characteristic lithology, long since
termed Pennant. The authors are reluctant to see this name
disappear . . . they accordingly propose that the term Pennant
Measures be introduced . . .' (Woodland and others 1957).

There is no reason why Pennant Grit (or Sandstone, etc.)
should not be retained as a formation with diachronic boundaries occurring within the Upper Coal Measures. The fact
is that the old Geological Survey maps of South Wales (whatever the intentions of their makers) showed diachronic subdivisions of the Coal Measures, while the new ones show (as
far as possible) units with isochronous boundaries. Geological
maps may show either kind of subdivision, or both in different
parts of the succession. In the coalfields units with isochronous
boundaries are preferable, since these boundaries correspond
with, or are parallel to, coal seams. This does not mean that
diachronic units are useless, for they serve a separate purpose
in describing the lithological development which is often of
more immediate importance for the uses to which geological
maps are put.

Another example of diachronism is provided by the Devonian
of New York State. According to the present interpretation
shown in Figure 24 grey and brown shales and sandstones of
the upper part of the succession (Chemung, Canadaway, Con-
neaut, Conewango) pass laterally into red beds (Catskill
facies), the lower units doing so only at the eastern end of
the section while higher members do so progressively further
west. Thus at any particular part of the section grey and
brown beds are succeeded by red beds, so that when they were
first studied the former became known as the Chemung Group
and the latter as the Catskill Group, the assumption being
that the whole of the Catskill was younger than the Chemung.
According to current ideas the base of the Catskill in the
extreme east is actually older than the base of the Chemung
in the west!

The Devonian of New York State has presented problems
of nomenclature similar to those of the Permian of New
Mexico mentioned above (p. 107). There would seem to be
nothing wrong in principle in accepting Catskill Group as

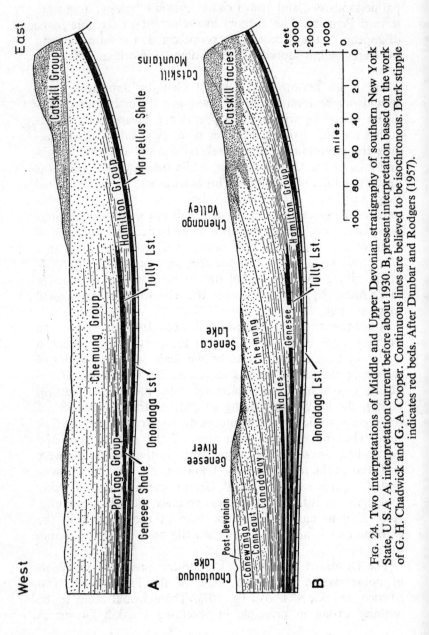

FIG. 24. Two interpretations of Middle and Upper Devonian stratigraphy of southern New York State, U.S.A. A, interpretation current before about 1930. B, present interpretation based on the work of G. H. Chadwick and G. A. Cooper. Continuous lines are believed to be isochronous. Dark stipple indicates red beds. After Dunbar and Rodgers (1957).

a diachronous unit. Yet stratigraphers have clearly felt uneasy about doing this. There is a recurring tendency among stratigraphers to be alarmed when a formation is discovered to be diachronous, and to feel that something ought to be done to make the terminology more precise in a time sense. This tendency, natural as it may be, must be resisted if the fundamental basis of stratigraphical classification is to be preserved. As I have already emphasized, both rock-units and time-units have their place and they must not be confused with each other.

6

BREAKS IN THE SUCCESSION

I HAVE already pointed out that much of the difficulty in establishing full successions arises from the fact that local successions are usually incomplete. The sedimentary succession in any place may be incomplete for one or both of two reasons: there may have been no deposition of sediment for a certain span of time, or rocks already deposited may have been removed by erosion. Breaks vary in size from very small to those involving a major part of geological time. It is usual, however, to distinguish two broad categories: a lesser known as *non-sequences* and a greater called *unconformities*. In the non-sequence non-deposition is the dominant factor, in the unconformity erosion plays an important part as well. These are not rigid categories, but they are a convenient if arbitrary way of classifying breaks in the succession. I shall say something about unconformities first, and consider non-sequences in the second part of the chapter.

James Hutton (1726–1797) was the first person to understand and explain the significance of unconformity. In 1787 he discovered an exposure in the Isle of Arran, Scotland, where the Calciferous Sandstone, of Carboniferous age, rests on metamorphic rocks of the Dalradian Series. Later in the same year, at Jedburgh near the English border, he found a place where older sediments, tilted to a high angle, are overlain by younger sediments lying horizontally. We now know that the two formations are of Silurian and Upper Old Red Sandstone age respectively. It is clear that the Silurian rocks were not only tilted, but also partly removed by erosion, before the Old Red Sandstone was deposited. This relationship was termed *unconformity* by the Edinburgh geologist Robert Jameson in 1805 and later became known as *angular unconformity* on account of the difference in angle of dip between the lower and upper sediments.

At Hutton's Jedburgh unconformity, as at many others, the surface of contact between the upper and lower formations is more or less flat. From this circumstance, perhaps, arose the expression *plane of unconformity*, a misnomer since the contact is never a true plane and is sometimes very irregular. The flatness of some unconformities, however, is certainly striking. Erosional forms like this are rare on land, but common in areas of rock bottom in shallow seas where they are assumed to result from marine erosion (Fig. 25). Accordingly, flat surfaces of unconformity can often be ascribed to the same cause. The deposits overlying them are often marine, and the erosion and subsequent deposition may sometimes be consecutive actions of the same sea. Conditions in which sedimentation follows erosion at any one place may be provided by a transgressing sea. The basal conglomerates which sometimes cover flat surfaces of unconformity are usually explained as beach gravels left behind as the sea advanced, buried by later deposits.

At some unconformities the discordance in dip is large and the unconformity obvious. In other cases the discordance is slight and the existence of an unconformity is only revealed by mapping. A good example is the unconformity at the base of the Gault in south-west England, shown in Figure 2. The difference in dip between the Gault and the underlying Jurassic rocks is less than a degree, and is not measurable at sections where the contact is exposed. Mapping shows that the base of the Gault transgresses across various Jurassic formations, the oldest being the Oxford Clay (in the west) and the youngest the Portland Beds (in the east). We infer that the Jurassic rocks were tilted towards the east, and a surface of erosion cut across them, before the Gault was deposited. Nearly 1,000 feet of Jurassic beds have been removed at the westernmost extension of the Gault. These are still present about 15 miles to the east. This situation where the younger formation comes to rest in turn on various formations of a tilted or folded older group is known as *overstep*. In this case the *rate of overstep*, calculated from the figures mentioned above, is about 60 feet thickness of underlying beds per mile, corresponding to a dip of the Jurassic rocks of about two-thirds of a degree greater than that of the Gault. Thus a very slight discordance in dip can result in an important effect if it persists over a large enough area.

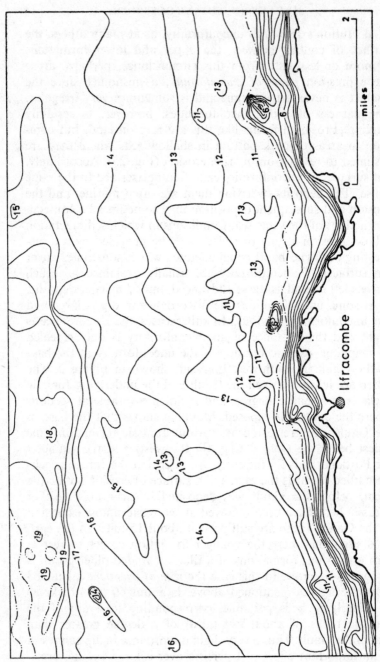

FIG. 25. Contour map of the sea floor off north Devon. Contour interval = one fathom. The area shown is largely floored by rock. Based on Admiralty Survey No. E.8675 with the sanction of the Hydrographer of the Navy.

The relationship of the Cambrian to the Pre-Cambrian in Montana is another example (Fig. 26). At individual exposures the Flathead Sandstone, of Middle Cambrian age, appears conformable on underlying rocks. Study of a wide area, however, shows that it oversteps onto older and older formations as one traces it from west to east. The discordance in dip at this unconformity appears to be about 2°, partly due to a general easterly thinning of the Pre-Cambrian. Although inconspicuous at exposures, the unconformity records an episode of erosion which has removed about 20,000 feet of beds in the east as compared with the west, and has been used to support the dating of the Belt group as Pre-Cambrian, on the grounds that considerable time must have been needed for the erosion to take place.

A uniform dip, whether high or low, of the rocks below an unconformity is seldom found. If the older rocks have been folded the discordance of dip is greatest over the limbs of the folds and vanishes over the crests and troughs, producing a local appearance of conformity at these points. This special case of apparent conformity was termed *disconformity* by Grabau in 1905 and *parallel unconformity* by some later authors. The value of such terms is discussed below. The lesson to be noted from this, as from the cases previously mentioned, is that an unconformity cannot be fully appreciated from a single outcrop or a small area; a regional study is usually needed, and the wider the area covered, the more complete will be the knowledge of the unconformity. Apparent conformity also occurs where horizontal beds have been dissected by erosion before the younger sediments were laid down (Fig. 27). Such a case would be termed unconformity by most geologists although there is no appreciable discordance in dip.

In the cases mentioned so far the base of the rocks above the unconformity has been assumed to be of unvarying age. If the upper beds were deposited following a rapid transgression over an area of low relief, this assumption may be substantially true. If the transgression was more gradual, or the relief considerable, sedimentation will have begun earlier in some places than in others. The larger the area concerned, the smaller is the probability that deposition started at the same time throughout the area.

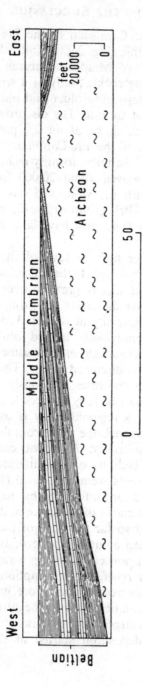

FIG. 26. The unconformity at the base of the Middle Cambrian in western Montana, U.S.A. The Middle Cambrian oversteps Beltian sediments at a rate of about 400 feet per mile. The thickness of the Middle Cambrian is exaggerated. After Deiss (1935).

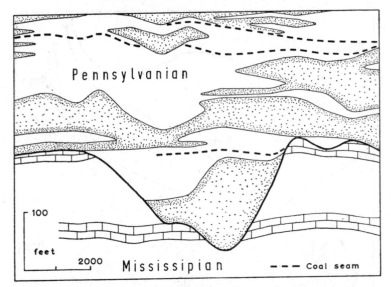

Fig. 27. Unconformity (shown by thick line) between Pennsylvanian and Mississippian sediments in south-eastern Illinois, U.S.A. Section based on 13 well-sections. Vertical scale exaggerated approx. × 17. After Potter and Desborough (1965).

The simplest case, in theory at least, will be found when the sea transgresses gradually across a surface of low relief. Each unit deposited by the transgressing sea will extend further than the underlying one, and come to rest in its turn upon the older rocks. This relationship is known as *overlap*. An example is provided by rocks of the Eocene Lutetian Stage of the Paris region, which form a very fossiliferous limestone formation known as the *calcaire grossier*. Within the formation R. Abrard distinguished four zones, and by studying their distribution demonstrated a steady southward transgression of the sea across the area during the Lutetian (Fig. 28), each zone overlapping the previous one and coming to rest in turn on pre-Lutetian rocks.

Where the surface of unconformity is irregular overlap is often found, since sediments of the younger group tend to accumulate first in the hollows and bury the hills later. In Somerset, England, the Palaeozoic rocks were strongly folded by the Variscan orogeny and the ensuing denudation left a

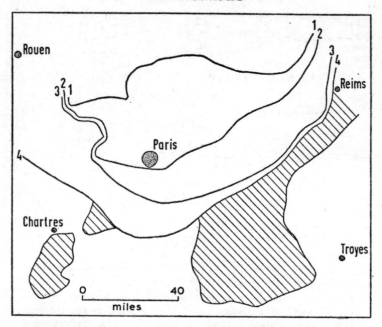

FIG. 28. Southward overlap of successive zones of the Eocene Lutetian Stage in the central part of the Paris basin. 1, southern limit of Zone of *Nummulites laevigatus* and *N. lamarcki*; 2, of Zone of *N. laevigatus*; 3, of Zone of *Echinolampas calvimontanus* and *Echinantus issyaviensis*; 4, of Zone of *Orbitolites complanatus*. Diagonal ruling indicates areas of continental deposition not covered by the Lutetian sea. After Abrard (1925).

relief of at least 1,000 feet. Sedimentation re-commenced during the Triassic period and continued in the Jurassic. All the valleys are filled with Triassic rocks which did not, however, cover the summits. The Rhaetic Beds overlap the Trias on to Palaeozoic rocks, and the Lias overlaps the Rhaetic, while a few areas of Palaeozoic remained uncovered till Middle Jurassic times (Fig. 29). Similarly in Figure 27 it is clear that Pennsylvanian sedimentation began in the valley and gradually buried the old landscape.

In the examples given so far the rocks both above and below the unconformity are sedimentary. Unconformity may also be present between a group of sediments and underlying igneous or metamorphic rocks. There will seldom be any difficulty about detecting such unconformity at exposures. Where the older rocks are metamorphic, or plutonic or hypabyssal igneous, it is clear that erosion must have operated to expose them at the surface for the younger series to be deposited on them. With lavas and pyroclastic rocks some kind of stratification is usually present and we can apply the same physical criteria as we do to sediments. The case where the lower group of rocks is not bedded was classed as *nonconformity* by M. Billings in 1942, but this term has also had other geological meanings including that of angular unconformity. The expression *heterolithic unconformity* (literally, of different lithology), proposed by S. I. Tomkeieff (1963) but is not self-explanatory since sedimentary rocks above and below an angular unconformity are often heterolithic. On the whole it seems better to avoid such special terms, because of

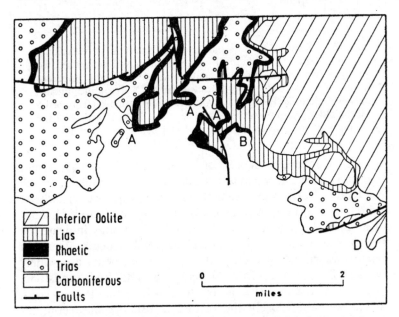

Inferior Oolite
Lias
Rhaetic
Trias
Carboniferous
Faults

0   2
miles

FIG. 29. Geological map of part of south-east Somerset, England, to show overlap of Mesozoic formations. At A Rhaetic overlaps Trias on to the Carboniferous; at B Lias overlaps Rhaetic. Inferior Oolite overlaps Lias on to Trias at C, and overlaps Trias on to Carboniferous at D. Based on Crown Copyright Geological Survey map by permission of the Controller of H.M. Stationery Office.

the inconsistency in their use, and employ straightforward descriptive or qualifying adjectives when it is necessary to be precise. Figure 30 shows some of the kinds of unconformity

Because earth movements are likely to have affected the course of sedimentation, unconformities are important for working out the tectonic history of the earth's crust. The assumption usually made is that uplift will slow down or terminate sedimentation, and may cause it to be replaced by

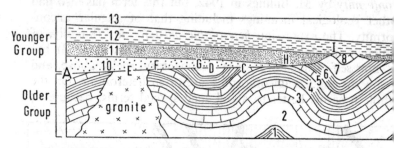

FIG. 30. Diagram to illustrate some terms used in describing unconformities. A surface of unconformity A-B separates two groups of rocks. At C there is angular unconformity, at D apparent conformity (parallel unconformity), at E 'heterolithic unconformity'. Between F and G the younger group oversteps from bed 5 of the older group on to bed 6 and then bed 7. At H bed 11 of the younger group overlaps bed 10, and at I bed 12 overlaps bed 11.

erosion. Conversely depression or downwarping may permit unusually thick sedimentary sequences to accumulate, which will tend to have fewer breaks than thinner sequences elsewhere. Both effects are important for working out the tectonic history of an area. In general, a major unconformity may indicate the occurrence locally of important earth movements. Thus, in north-western Europe the Caledonian movements are widely marked by the unconformity below the Old Red Sandstone, and the Variscan orogeny by that below the Permo-Trias. When we look closely the picture is usually more complex than this. Movements may have begun gently, resulting perhaps in shallowing of the sea before sedimentation actually ceased, and may have taken a long time to die away afterwards, while even during intense tectonic activity 'synorogenic' sediments may have accumulated elsewhere. Frequently, therefore, the dating of earth movements provided in this way is not very close, especially if the time-gap represented by the unconformity is large. In the example in Somerset mentioned above and shown in Figure 29 the youngest rocks seen below the unconformity are late Upper Carboniferous and the oldest rocks above it are probably late Trias, so that a length of time equal roughly to two geological periods is unrepresented. It is usually assumed that the earlier part of this interval was occupied by earth movements and the later part by denudation, but there is no evidence as to the date of the earth movements within the interval. We still have little idea of the length of time tectonic episodes take, although a picture of an orogeny as a series of episodes building up to a climax and then dying away can be assembled from sections over a wide area. Least information may be obtained where earth movements were most intense.

If, as often happens, both overstep and overlap occur, the span of geological time represented by an unconformity is continuously variable and neither the upper or lower limit of this span is of constant age. The unconformities involving the greatest length of time are not always the most conspicuous. For example, in parts of the Grand Canyon of Colorado the early Carboniferous Redwall Limestone rests on Middle Cambrian Muav Limestone with scarcely any discordance of dip: at exposures the two formations appear conformable: yet more than three geological systems are missing between them. By contrast, striking angular unconformities sometimes represent short time spans. In the Midland Valley of Scotland Lower Old Red Sandstone rests with strong unconformity on Upper Silurian rocks. Naturally the first kind of unconformity is liable to occur in stable areas subject mainly to epeirogenic movements, while the second kind is likely to be found in orogenic belts.

NON-SEQUENCES

Non-sequences are, in general, not readily revealed by gross physical relationships as unconformities often are. They are most commonly detected as a result of detailed palaeontological zoning. They began to be appreciated in the second half of the last century as subdivision and correlation by fossils, inspired by Oppel's work on the Jurassic of north-west Europe, began to gather momentum. In England, S. S. Buckman working on the Middle Jurassic in the 1880s and 1890s found that he could distinguish a large number of palaeontological subdivisions, but that the full set was not everywhere present—at many places one or more subdivisions were represented by a non-sequence. No doubt other workers were reaching similar conclusions at other places and in other geological systems.

Non-sequences may be detected by palaeontological or physical criteria, or by both. It may happen that, in a particular section, two fossil zones are in contact which are known elsewhere to be separated by intervening zones. There must have been a break in sedimentation even though there is no physical evidence for one. The Lias of north-west Europe can be subdivided in great detail by means of ammonites: about 20 zones are established and most of these can be subdivided, at least over limited areas, into subzones. Study of the zones shows that many non-sequences are present, of variable geographical extent. In general the sequence is most nearly complete where it is thickest, and reduction of thickness is accompanied by the appearance of non-sequences as well as by thinning of individual zones. The thick sequences are believed to have accumulated in subsiding areas, the thinner ones in areas where subsidence was smaller or intermittent (Fig. 19). In such areas the sea floor may have remained for periods of time too shallow for deposition to take place. In Britain non-sequences get noticeably larger and more numerous towards the London area, which was land in Liassic times.

The pattern seen in the European Lias is found in other formations where fossil zoning is sufficiently precise. No doubt it is present in many more which are either too sparsely fossiliferous, or lack suitable zonal forms, for the breaks to be detected.

In Jameson Land, East Greenland (Fig. 11), where a series of near-horizontal clastic Mesozoic sediments outcrop, the Upper Vardeklöft Formation (Borealis-Calloviense Zones) is succeeded by the Black Series (Plicatilis and higher Zones) with no significant lithological change. In fact, as shown in Figure 11, correlation of the local ammonite sequence with the European zones suggests that six zones are missing, and that there is a non-sequence between the two formations.

Occasionally a non-sequence may be detected from fossil evidence without reference to any sequence elsewhere. A sudden change of fauna should arouse suspicion, although it may often be due to other factors such as change of facies or migration of new forms into the area. Where fossils both above and below the suspected break belong to the same group, however, and especially if a pattern of steady evolutionary change is suddenly interrupted, we may suspect a non-sequence with some reason. A classic case is provided by R. Brinkmann's study (1929) of ammonites of the family Kosmoceratidae in part of the Oxford Clay (Upper Jurassic) at Peterborough, England. Having collected a large number of specimens, recording the horizon of each above a reference level, he studied the variation of several characters with horizon. The graphs showed discontinuities at certain horizons, because the record of part of the evolutionary changes in the lineage was missing. From the slope of the graph the thickness of sediment which would have accumulated if there had been no break could be estimated. Summaries of this work have been given by Dunbar and Rodgers (1957) and Woodford (1963).

Brinkmann's technique could be used in other formations containing sufficiently abundant fossils of a group which was evolving fairly rapidly, and which bore easily measurable characters. The necessary combination of circumstances does not commonly occur, and the work is tedious, so that the method remains rather a stratigraphical curiosity than a normal technique. It is important, however, because it reminds us that there must be many breaks which remain undetected for want of sufficiently sensitive criteria.

Other criteria sometimes show up non-sequences. Living organisms may have flourished during a break in sedimentation and left their remains or their traces. In particular, sessile or encrusting animals of various kinds may spread across the sea floor, and beds of oysters or horizons with numerous crinoid roots, for example, may result. Burrowing or boring animals may be active, and although their work is often seen in sedimentary rocks an unusual concentration is suggestive of a hiatus in deposition. It often appears that some lithification took place before the succeeding beds were deposited, for example, when there are burrows of rock-boring animals like *Polydora* or *Pholas*, or sessile organisms known to favour a hard substrate. In these cases the evidence for a time-gap is strong. Condensed or remanié beds of fossils show that organic remains were accumulating although sediment was not.

Levels at which there is physical evidence for slight erosion are fairly common in the stratigraphical succession. In formations where the bedding-planes are uneven, a planed surface may be conspicuous, and suggest slight marine erosion. More severe erosion may truncate bedding planes or sedimentary structures, or may channel the beds already deposited. Thus the 'washouts' long known from coal-bearing strata evince erosion before a new sedimentary cycle began. Such intervals of erosion often separate cycles of sedimentation in other facies as well.

Physical evidence of slight erosion is provided by the rocks glorified under the names of *intraformational conglomerates* and *penecontemporaneous breccias*. Often the lowest part of a bed contains pieces of rock identical with that forming the bed below, although the two beds appear conformable. Although erosion has taken place such occurrences are usually held to mark non-sequences rather than unconformities, because they are commonly of small lateral extent.

DIASTEMS

A philosophical approach to the imperfection of the sedimentary record was made in the United States by J. Barrell (1917). Taking the greatest recorded thicknesses of the geological systems in relation to their duration indicated by radioactivity, Barrell calculated (as have other geologists) a mean rate of sedimentation throughout Phanerozoic time which was extremely slow (it is about one foot in 1,500 years). In most areas the thicknesses of the systems is much less than the maximum and the mean rate even slower, often by a factor of five or ten. This is at variance with observation which tells us that many ancient and modern sediments accumulated rapidly. Barrell inferred that the sedimentary record contains many minor, undetected breaks due to non-deposition or slight erosion. He invented the term *diastem* for these breaks.

Individual diastems are usually small and the majority are undetectable. Many bedding planes mark diastems (see also p. 73) for they usually resulted from interruptions in deposition. The discontinuities detected by Brinkmann in the Oxford Clay, described above, are examples of a kind that would normally pass undetected.

Some workers have regarded diastem as synonymous with non-sequence. The correctness of this is uncertain, since diastem is a theoretical concept while a non-sequence is a break which is demonstrated by palaeontological or physical evidence.

STRATIGRAPHICAL SIGNIFICANCE OF BREAKS

Breaks in the succession are both a nuisance and an advantage to the stratigrapher. Their nuisance-value has been mentioned and is obvious; they hinder the stratigrapher in one of his most important tasks, the establishment of a biostratigraphical succession which is as complete as possible. When we turn to the task of describing local successions of formations, breaks usually afford the best-defined and least disputed boundaries. More nearly continuous deposition often produced successions in which vertical changes are gradual or take the form of complex interfingering, so that formation boundaries are difficult to define. Unconformities invariably correspond with formation boundaries, and often with boundaries between larger lithostratigraphical units. Non-sequences too may form convenient boundaries, but there are many non-sequences and diastems within formations.

Because of their variable age limits unconformities are unsuited to be the boundaries of biostratigraphical units—zones, stages and (*a fortiori*) systems—which have isochronous boundaries. Naturally this is a counsel of perfection and local boundaries of such units may unavoidably be non-sequences or unconformities. Most systems were originally defined by unconformities because these were obvious and easily traceable boundaries to the early geologists. With the change in status of the system from a lithostratigraphical to a biostratigraphical unit (p. 149) unconformities have become obsolete as boundaries.

STRATIGRAPHICAL TERMS IN COMMON USE

Geological time terms	*Biostratigraphical terms*
Era	—
Period	System
Epoch	Series
Age	Stage
—	Substage
—	ZONE
—	Subzone

Terms placed opposite to one another correspond and have the same names, e.g. Jurassic Period, Jurassic System.

Lithostratigraphical terms

Group, Series* (also many
FORMATION informal units)
Member,† Lentil,† Tongue†

* Not accepted in this sense by the International Subcommission (Statement of Principles) or in the American Code, but in common use.
† Chiefly in North America.

7

CLASSIFICATION

WILLIAM SMITH recognized over forty distinct strata, but did not group them into larger assemblages. During his lifetime, however, other geologists started to do so, as knowledge of the sedimentary succession developed and more and more strata were distinguished. William Buckland (1784–1856) in 1818 grouped the strata into larger categories to form a hierarchy: Class, Order, Formation and Stratum (Fig. 31), a unit of any category except the lowest containing units of the next lower in the series. The names of the categories of the hierarchy, and their meanings, have changed since Buckland, but the principle remains in operation today. Later in the nineteenth century the same thing happened to biostratigraphical and geological-time units. In 1878 stratigraphical classification and terminology were considered at the First International Geological Congress held in Paris, which attempted to formulate a standard hierarchy of terms. Subsequent Congresses and other bodies have reconsidered the matter, and the latest pronouncement was at the Twenty-first Congress at Copenhagen in 1960. The full history of these deliberations will not be given here; they have been summarized by Dunbar and Rodgers (1957, ch. 17) and Holland (1964).

The distinction between rock units and time units was made early in the history of geology and was recognized in 1881 by the Second International Geological Congress. The term *biostratigraphy*, for stratigraphy based on palaeontology, seems to have been invented by the Belgian palaeontologist L. Dollo and defined in its modern sense in 1910, but did not become current in English-language discussion of the subject until much later. As diachronism began to be widely appreciated and the tracing of lateral facies change became common, the need to keep distinct isochronous units, provided by fossil

ORDER OF SUPERPOSITION OF STRATA IN THE BRITISH ISLANDS.

By Rev. W. BUCKLAND, B.D. F.R.S. M.G.S. Fellow of C.C.C. and Professor of Mineralogy in Oxford:

CLASS I.—*Alluvium.*

FORMATIONS.	NAMES.	CHARACTER.	LOCALITIES.	Greatest observed thickness in feet.
		Superficial Deposits composed irregularly of the Debris of all Formations.		
No. 1. Alluvium.	Post-diluvian Detritus. { Blown Sand.	Sand and comminuted Shells drifted inland by winds from the sea shore, sometimes partially consolidated, and sometimes forming Doons.	Perran-Zabulo, Bude, and Porth Towan, Cornwall. Newbiggen, Northumberland.	
	Fluviatile Detritus. { Mud Sand and Silt. { Gravel Sand and Mud from the neighbouring hills.		Deltas at the mouths of rivers. Inland Channels of torrents and rapid rivers.	
	Diluvian Detritus.	Sand Clay and Gravel composed of fragments both of neighbouring hills and of distant rocks, containing bones of the Elephant, Rhinoceros, Ox, Deer, Hippopotamus, &c. not mineralized.	Every where in vallies, often on summits and slopes of hills and on elevated plains. Walton, Essex; Harwich; London; Brentford; Oxford; Gloucester,	

CLASS II.—*Trap Rocks.*

		Intruding themselves into all formations (except Class 1) in irregular beds, masses, and dykes.		
No. 2. Trap Formation.	Flötz Trap.	Basalt, Wacke, Amygdaloid, Greenstone, Clink-Stone, Trap-Tuff, Pitchstone, Ochre, &c.	Giants' Causeway, Antrim; and Benyevenagh, Derry; in beds above chalk. Campsey and Ochill Hills, Scotland.	1040
	Whin Dykes.		Whin Dykes, Passim; coast of Antrim; Isle of Arran; Cockfield Dyke, Durham; Vale of Berkley, Gloucestershire.	

CLASS III.—Secondary Rocks.

Containing abundantly Organic Remains and Fragments of older Rocks.

ORDER I. HORIZONTAL.

Strata regular and nearly horizontal, made up of alternations of Clay, Marl, Pebbles, Sand, and Limestone.

No. 3. Formations above Chalk. 3rd Gypsum Formation of Werner.	Upper Freshwater Beds.	Yellow argillaceous Limestone with Clay and Sand (contains Freshwater Shells).	Headon Hill, and Bembridge Ledge, Isle of Wight.	122
	Upper Marine Beds.	Clay and Marl (with Marine Shells).	Headon Hill.	36
	Lower Freshwater Beds.	Sandy and argillaceous Limestone (contains Freshwater Shells).	Headon Hill.	63
	London Clay.	Lead-coloured Clay with Septaria. Calcareous Sandstone, containing Green Earth. Clay, containing Fossils, the same with those of the Calcaire grossier of Paris.	Sheppy Island, Kent. Bognor Rocks, Sussex. Hordwell Cliff, near Christchurch, Hants. Highgate Hill, Richmond Hill.	550
	Plastic Clay.	Potters Clay, white, blue, and red, alternating with beds of Sand containing Green Earth, and of Gravel made up of rolled Chalk Flints.	Blackheath, Kent; Reading, Berks; Corfe Castle; Alum Bay, Isle of Wight.	1131
No. 4. Chalk Formation. 3rd Lime, or Pläner Kalkstein of Werner?	Upper Chalk.	With many beds of flinty Nodules, and soft enough to mark with.	Salisbury Plain. Downs of Sussex. {Surface water-worn into irregular hollows under Plastic Clay.}	320
	Lower Chalk.	With few Flints, and harder than Upper Chalk; sometimes used as a Building Stone.	Near Warminster. Shakespear's Cliff, Dover. Flamborough Head, Yorkshire. County of Antrim, Ireland.	360
	Chalk Marl, Malm, or Grey Chalk.	Argillaceous Grey Chalk, without Flints or Chert, passing into fine micaceous Grey Sand. —— into Grey Clay, and Marl.	Benson, Oxon; Cherhill and Norton Bavant, Wilts; Lewes; Guildford. Folkstone. Ryarsh near Wrotham, Kent.	200

FIG. 31. Part of the classification of strata by William Buckland published by William Phillips (1818).

zones, and local lithology became clear. Two American authors, H. G. Schenck and S. W. Muller (1941), made clear the desirability of a dual classification, into lithostratigraphical or local rock-units, on the one hand, and biostratigraphical units for general correlation on the other. Since then there has been extensive discussion, mainly in North America, on the problem of standardizing the stratigraphical hierarchy. In 1946 was formed the American Commission on Stratigraphical Nomenclature, representing the principal geological surveys and professional associations. After a number of preliminary reports a Code of Stratigraphic Nomenclature was published in 1961 (referred to hereafter as the 'American Code').

Britain has been more hesitant in codifying practice but in 1964 the Geological Society of London set up a Subcommittee 'to consider recommendations for a British code of stratigraphical practice' (*Proc. Geol. Soc.*, no. 1620, p. 24). Their final report has not yet been issued.

Although national codes may be valuable, international agreement would clearly be preferable because the basic principles and methods of stratigraphy are the same everywhere. An International Subcommission on Stratigraphic Terminology was set up by the International Congress in 1952, and has produced a Statement of Principles and a glossary of terms (Hedberg 1961) which was intended to serve as a preliminary step towards the eventual preparation of an international code. There were dissentients from the report of whom the chief was the USSR Stratigraphical Commission. The Subcommission's proposals are mentioned in the following pages. The Russian code is described at the end of the chapter.

These attempts to regularize usage have met with certain inevitable difficulties. To begin with a large number of stratigraphical names, not conforming to any uniform scheme, were in existence by the time the first code was formulated. Then the sequences of sedimentary rocks which have to be named and classified differ greatly between themselves, so that what is a suitable arrangement in one case may not be so in another. On account of this variation it is difficult to make critical comparisons between practice in different parts of the succession and different areas. Subdivisions of a thick, monotonous sequence of geosynclinal sediments may be one hundred or one thousand times the thickness of those recognized in a thin, condensed, sequence, although they may have comparable ranges in time. Should both have the same rank in the hierarchy? A unit of a certain rank may have two subdivisions in one case, twenty in another. Increase of knowledge or economic interest may result in the subdivision of a unit previously undivided, and it should be possible to do this without disturbing the existing classification.

THE DEFINITION OF STRATIGRAPHICAL UNITS

Any unit in a stratigraphical hierarchy, except the smallest, may be defined in either of two ways: directly, by a statement of what it includes in terms of beds at a specified section or by its fossil fauna, or indirectly, in terms of the units of next lower rank that it contains. These alternatives have been named the *typological* and *hierarchical* methods respectively by J. H. Callomon (1964). Units in the lowest class must be defined typologically. It is usual, in systems of classification, for all higher classes to be defined hierarchically.

The lowest lithostratigraphical unit for this purpose is the formation, lower units (members, tongues, etc.) being regarded as informal and not used in every case. The American Code states that the definition of a lithostratigraphical unit should be 'based on as full knowledge as possible of its lateral and vertical variations'—in other words, in terms of a map or other synthesis—but that 'for purposes of nomenclatural stability a type section should be designated'. On account of lateral change of lithology and diachronism a type section cannot fully define a formation, but can only indicate its limits at one place. Traced away from the type section there may or may not be agreement among different geologists as to the limits, depending on how clear-cut they are and on the lithological complexity of the case. I have mentioned earlier (p. 19) the proviso in the American Code that a formation should be a mappable unit.

Zones, the basic units of the biostratigraphical hierarchy, are defined typologically by their characteristic fossil or fossils. In its simplest form such a definition may consist merely of a

K

list of species. It is more useful to explain which of the specie
are restricted to the zone, which range through the whole o
it and which characterize certain parts. In practice this in
formation may take the form of actual sections or table
showing the ranges of the fossils, but it is the palaeontologica
definition and not the stratal one which is important. The bed
placed in a certain zone at a certain section may be changed
new discoveries extend the range of the characteristic fauna.

In practice stages and series are defined in terms of zones
they are defined according to the hierarchical method. Th
International Subcommission and the American Commissio
do not recognize this. They describe stages, series and system
as *chronostratigraphical* units which they regard as of a di
ferent kind from biostratigraphical zones. This distinction
not accepted here, as explained on page 157. The Statement o
Principles and the American Code, while they agree that zone
are defined typologically by fauna as stated in the last para
graph, propose that 'chronostratigraphical' units be define
typologically in terms of type sections. Once the independen
definition of units in two classes of the hierarchy is concede
stages are not related to zones and stage boundaries need no
coincide with zonal boundaries. This is contrary to actua
usage and could produce confusion. Furthermore, as a resu
different criteria (hierarchical and typological) are alread
being used by different geologists to define stages and the
is no common ground between them, thus adding to th
difficulty of settling disputes over boundaries. That this is no
a mere hypothetical fear is shown by the case of the Bajocia
Stage of which a new definition, quite different from pr
existing ones, has been recently produced as a result of th
study of a supposed type section, as explained later (p. 168
The danger of the application of these new codes to long
established biostratigraphical units is a real one: the attemp
to define these units from type sections does not resolv
disputes, it merely adds new complications.

A further difficulty with the typological approach is tha
many stages do not have type sections defined with sufficie
precision by their authors, who could not foresee the futur
progress of stratigraphy. For example, several of d'Orbigny
Jurassic stages were named after English localities which h

never visited. Bath and Kellaways are unsuited to be type localities for the Bathonian and Callovian Stages, and while the upper part of the Kimmeridgian Stage is well exposed on the coast near Kimmeridge, Dorset, the lower part is below sea level. Once other localities have to be chosen the choice in many cases is little more than arbitrary.

Difficulty may also arise if the upper boundary of one stage at one type section does not correspond with the lower boundary of the next at its type section, as defined by their respective authors. Even if stages are defined hierarchically, as including specified zones, boundary problems may arise if new zones are discovered which fall between two stages as currently defined. The way to avoid this dilemma is to define the base only of each stage, a practice followed as early as 1879 by Lapworth and recently re-affirmed by the British Mesozoic Committee (Ager 1963). If only the bases of stages are defined, any beds earlier than the base automatically fall into the underlying stage, and if agreement on the definitions of stages can once be reached, the permanency of the scheme is assured.

I maintain here that stages and higher classes of units which are assumed to have isochronous boundaries can in practice only be defined in the hierarchical fashion, in terms of their included zones. This does not remove the necessity for a type section or area, for zonal schemes are usually of limited geographical extent while higher classes should, if possible, be world-wide (p. 151). The definition, however, is in faunal and not lithological terms. To summarize, a stage is defined in terms of a zonal scheme in a certain area, where its limits may be well-defined if the zonal scheme is a good one. Beyond the area for which the zones are valid the limits of the stage, determined by such correlations as can be made, may approximate less well to isochronous surfaces (Fig. 32).

Although formal definitions of higher classes must be hierarchical, we do in practice make use of typological definitions. For example, in southern England the Carboniferous Limestone Series consists of four groups (Fig. 17) which all consist (with minor exceptions) of limestone, in contrast to the Old Red Sandstone below and the Millstone Grit above. One can always recognize the Carboniferous Limestone in the field although one may not be able readily to identify the group which is present. Similarly the Sinemurian Stage in the Jurassic corresponds in north-west Europe with the range of the ammonite superfamily Arietitaceae, and can sometimes be recognized even if individual zones cannot be proved.

ROCK-STRATIGRAPHICAL UNITS

In Britain, on account of the informal character of stratigraphical nomenclature, many workers have managed without any regular hierarchy of rock units. It is possible to say that the Kinderscout Grit is a subdivision of the Millstone Grit without saying—or even thinking—what rank is assigned to each. It can be argued that such looseness of terminology is well suited to the phenomena which stratigraphy has to describe, and is valuable when stratigraphical units vary widely in size and importance and may be classified in different ways even in different parts of one system.

In North America there has been more conscious use of a regular scale of terms. The hierarchy in general use, and proposed by the International Subcommission is:

> Group
> > Formation
> > > Member (lentil, tongue)
> > > Bed

The Subcommission proposes flexibility in the use of this scheme: 'Formations need not be aggregated into groups' and 'a formation need not be divided into members unless a useful purpose is thus served. Some formations may be divided completely into members; others may have only certain parts designated as members; still others may have no members' (Hedberg 1961).

The chief departure from the proposed standard scheme in British practice is the frequent use of *series* as a lithostratigraphical term: for example Carboniferous Limestone Series, Bunter Series. In other British instances it is used in a biostratigraphical sense, as in the Lower Palaeozoic, and in many instances it is difficult to know what meaning of the term is intended.

BIOSTRATIGRAPHICAL UNITS

The classification of units defined in terms of fossils, or bio-stratigraphical units, has been mentioned in Chapter 2. The basic unit is universally agreed to be the zone. The full scale of terms proposed by the International Subcommission is:

> Erathem
> System
> Series
> Stage
> Substage
> Zone

The Subcommission divides these terms between two categories, chronostratigraphical and biostratigraphical, a distinction which is not adopted here as explained on page 157. Erathem, the biostratigraphical equivalent of era (p. 162), is not in general use. The others are widely accepted.

SYSTEMS

The *system* began to be used in England about 1820 for an assemblage of formations with certain characters in common: for example, Oolitic System for a group of formations in which oolite occurs at a number of horizons, although many other rock-types are also present, and Carboniferous System for rocks including coal seams. Murchison in 1839 divided the British succession 'into eight sedimentary groups, each of which I conceive (in British classification), to be entitled to be called "Systems", from their dimensions, lithological charac-ters, and zoological contents. In comparing, however, the rocks of our own land with those of foreign countries, it is not con-tended that each of these systems has a general or even a European range'. It is desirable, however, that the major units used in different countries should correspond, and the systems adopted by Murchison, with the addition of others, were soon adopted internationally. The system thus changed its meaning, and from being a more or less local lithological grouping became the major unit of world-wide correlation, with boun-daries which are defined palaeontologically. This has led to controversy in some cases because a suitable zonal boundary may not coincide with the lithological change or unconformity by which a system was originally defined. The question of system boundaries is discussed in the next chapter.

There are still a few exceptions to the definition in the last paragraph, in areas where rocks for some reason (often because they are in non-marine facies) cannot be dated in terms of the standard geological systems. Thus we have the Gondwana System of India and the Karroo System of South Africa. The Old Red Sandstone of northern Europe may legitimately be considered a system in this sense, roughly but not exactly equivalent in time to the Devonian period. For the same reason, the impossibility of exact correlation, Pre-Cambrian sedimentary rocks may be classified into local systems, as the later Pre-Cambrian and early palaeozoic rocks of India are placed in the Cuddapah and Vindhyan Systems, separated by an unconformity.

The system thus can have two meanings: the universally recognized systems of the Phanerozoic are biostratigraphical units, but local systems may be either biostratigraphical, if their limits can be defined by fossil faunas, or lithostratigraphical if they cannot; they are bound to be the latter in the Pre-Cambrian.

The historical origins of the Phanerozoic systems have been summarized by M. G. Willmarth (1925).

SERIES

Although *series* is recognized in current codes as a biostratigraphical term, present usage is not consistent, as already remarked. Furthermore, it is seldom in practice that both series and stages are used, as will be shown later in this chapter. In most systems a threefold hierarchy: system, stage, zone, is all that is needed. For these reasons it would seem better to drop series as far as possible. The survival of the term in recent codes (from earlier codes which were less carefully defined) is to be regretted.

STAGES

Each of d'Orbigny's stages was a group of rocks characterized by a particular fossil fauna. The types of rock present varied from place to place, and it was implicit from d'Orbigny's belief in successive creations that the rocks of each stage were contemporaneous wherever they occurred and the base of the stage, defined by the appearance of the newly created fauna, was the same age everywhere. Although we can no longer accept such a foolproof criterion for the base of a stage, the term has come to be used for a division which can be recognized, under favourable circumstances, the world over. Arkell (1956) expressed the view of Mesozoic geologists:

'. . . it is convenient . . . to have a grouping which enables several zones to be correlated in a general way over long distances when the zones individually are too precise. Such groupings of zones are Stages. They transcend zones horizontally as well as vertically and provide a stratigraphical unit of wider use, adapted to intercontinental . . . correlations. Whereas the individual zone cannot be recognized beyond the area of occurrence of its index species or typical fauna, a stage can be followed all over the world by a series of overlapping correlations . . .'

Most of the Mesozoic stages can be identified in marine facies throughout the world.

In some systems many superfluous stage names have been proposed. They often originated with authors who coined names for local successions. In cases such as the Tertiary (p. 156) local stages must be used because of the difficulties of correlation. In general, however, they defeat d'Orbigny's object of providing a framework for universal correlation. For example at least 125 stage names have been used in the Jurassic, whereas a set of ten or a dozen is needed for world correlation. How should we choose the ones to be used and define their limits? Arkell in 1946 proposed, for the Jurassic and Cretaceous Systems at least, four rules to be used to produce a standard sequence:

1. Stage names to be founded on place names, either modern or latinized, and to end in -ian (French -ien). Names founded in other ways to be rejected.

2. Rule of priority: the date of publication (subject to rule 3) to be the deciding factor in choosing between alternative names.

3. Starting point in time to be the year 1850. In this year

was published the section of d'Orbigny's *Paléontologie française* in which a complete set of stages for the Jurassic was provided and defined.

4. Suspension of these rules to be resorted to in special cases where strict application would cause confusion or would result in the disappearance of familiar names.

Applied to the Jurassic System the rules result in the survival of d'Orbigny's original scheme with a few changes (p. 156). It seems doubtful whether they would produce good results if applied to systems in which stages have been proposed piecemeal by different authors at different times. They do not (and probably could not, even if added to) solve all the problems that arise. Many stages are nearly, but not exactly, the equivalents of others. Some, including some of d'Orbigny's, were inadequately defined by their authors. Such factors cause difficulties if Arkell's rule 2 were strictly applied and a large element of personal choice would remain. Arkell conceded that a single set of rules to cover all systems might be found to be impracticable, and geologists so far have shown little desire to consider the question deeply.

Current practice is to form stage-names from place-names or to their latinized forms. D'Orbigny also used personal names and lithological or palaeontological features (e.g. Murchisonian, Saliferian, Corallian) but none of these has survived. The place after which a stage is named is normally assumed to be the type-locality, but in many cases is of limited value for defining the stage (p. 146). Stage boundaries ideally coincide with prominent faunal changes: for example, the base of the Carnian stage of the Trias coincides with the appearance of many new ammonoid families and the Sinemurian in the Jurassic of north-west Europe begins with the first appearance of bisulcate ammonites, the arietitaceans, an easily recognizable level. Other boundaries are less well-marked, and some are little more than matters for arbitrary agreement. In some cases, such as the Toarcian-Bajocian boundary in the Jurassic, reviewed later on page 166, disagreement has been long-standing.

ZONES

Oppel fixed the zone as a subdivision of the stage. There are often five or six zones to a stage, although the number varies widely. For example:

Zones in
N.W. Europe

Sinemurian Stage
$\left\{\begin{array}{l}\text{Raricostatum} \\ \text{Oxynotum} \\ \text{Obtusum} \\ \text{Turneri} \\ \text{Semicostatum} \\ \text{Bucklandi}\end{array}\right.$

The subdivision and nomenclature of zones have been dealt with in Chapter 2.

DIVISION OF THE SYSTEMS INTO SERIES AND STAGES

The Lower Palaeozoic rocks are generally divided into series, although neither series nor stages have been much used in the Cambrian. The standard European subdivisions are named after places and date partly from R. I. Murchison and partly from later authors.

	Series	*Author*
Silurian System	Ludlow	Murchison 1833
	Wenlock	Murchison 1839
	Llandovery	Murchison 1859
Ordovician System	Ashgill	Marr 1905
	Caradoc	Murchison 1835
	Llandeilo	Murchison 1835
	Llanvirn	Hicks 1881
	Arenig	Sedgwick 1852
	Tremadoc	Sedgwick 1846

These names originally designated rock groups and Murchison, indeed, called them formations. With further study they became series each containing numerous formations. The series are now used as biostratigraphical units. Sometimes the ending -ian is added—Arenigian, Llanvirnian, etc.—but many authors do not do this.

In Britain some workers divide the Ordovician series into stages, following the example of B. B. Bancroft (1929 and later works) who divided the Caradoc Series into seven stages. Study of the duration in years of Bancroft's stages (p. 71)

suggests that they are much smaller units than stages in oth
systems.

For the Ordovician we have:

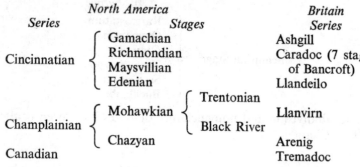

North America		Britain
Series	Stages	Series
Cincinnatian	Gamachian	Ashgill
	Richmondian	Caradoc (7 sta,
	Maysvillian	of Bancroft)
	Edenian	Llandeilo
Champlainian	Mohawkian { Trentonian	Llanvirn
	{ Black River	
	Chazyan	Arenig
Canadian		Tremadoc

This table merely compares two methods of subdivision a
does not indicate correlation. Each set of terms is well und
stood in its own country but is irritating for casual readers
the opposite side of the Atlantic. The average Briton readi
that a particular fossil or formation is Richmondian m
stop and work it out or look it up. When detailed correlati
has proceeded far enough an international scheme will
highly desirable, though whether either side will give way
the other is another matter.

Marine Devonian stratigraphers generally use stages a
zones after the Mesozoic pattern; separate and sometimes lo
stages are used for the Old Red Sandstone.

In the Carboniferous of Europe five stages are in u
Tournaisian, Viséan, Namurian, Westphalian and Stephani
They are large compared with the Mesozoic stages (see p
71), and some writers refer to them as series. In North Amer
the Mississippian System, nearly equivalent to Lower C
boniferous (=Tournaisian+Viséan), has been divided ir
four stages and the Pennsylvanian System, nearly equivale
to Upper Carboniferous, into five or six. In England
Namurian has been divided into six stages, Pendleian, Ar
bergian, Sabdenian, Kinderscoutian, Marsdenian and Y
donian. By implication the Namurian should be a series. T
other Carboniferous stages have not been subdivided, and
Namurian stage names have not been widely adopted outsi
the British Isles.

In Britain the Westphalian stage corresponds roughly to the Coal Measures, which have undergone an interesting change in stratigraphical status. The name was originally applied by W. D. Conybeare (1818) to the coal-bearing rocks overlying the Millstone Grit. With further study of the various coalfields it became the practice to divide the Coal Measures into three parts. In each coalfield this classification was a convenient local lithological grouping which was not intended to correlate with the subdivisions in other coalfields. The terms Lower Coal Measures, Middle Coal Measures and Upper Coal Measures were defined by different criteria in different coalfields. The Geological Survey of Great Britain therefore decided to re-define them in terms of marine bands, so that each division contained (as far as possible) rocks of the same age wherever it was recorded (Stubblefield and Trotter 1957). In doing this, however, they changed the old lithostratigraphical units into biostratigraphical units of undefined status. This is open to criticism because it introduces a new set of biostratigraphical terms which impedes, rather than assists, international correlation, for which purpose the British terms must be converted into the standard subdivisions of the Westphalian recognized on the continent of Europe:

	European divisions		British Geological Survey divisions	
	D	}	Upper	}
	upper C			
Westphalian {	lower C	}	Middle	} Coal Measures
	B			
	A		Lower	

Further, confusing nomenclature arises because the boundaries between the three divisions cannot be recognized in all coalfields. In the Bristol Coalfield the following scheme is in use (Welch and Trotter 1961):

Biostratigraphical units		Local formation names
Upper Coal Measures	{	Upper Coal Series
		Pennant Series
Middle Coal Measures	}	Lower Coal Series
Lower Coal Measures		

The term series is here used as a lithological term, but an American (for example) might be excused for thinking that the headings of the two columns above should be transposed!

In the Mesozoic there is a fair measure of agreement on the stage-names for world-wide correlation. Most of them have long been in use, although not always with unambiguous meanings.

Because of the unequal state of knowledge in d'Orbigny's time, his stages in the Palaeozoic were more or less equivalent to present-day systems, and have not passed into general use. The Jurassic and Cretaceous systems were known in greater detail and d'Orbigny's stages survive with modification to the present day. Thus for the Jurassic:

d'Orbigny 1842–1851	Arkell 1956
Portlandien	Portlandian
Kimméridgien	Kimmeridgian
Corallien ⎫ Oxfordien ⎭	Oxfordian
Callovien	Callovian
Bathonien	Bathonian
Bajocien	Bajocian
Toarcien	Toarcian
Liasien	Pliensbachian
Sinémurien ⎧ ⎩	Sinemurian Hettangian

Other names have been coined and used but there is a fair measure of agreement on Arkell's list and any worker on the Jurassic would understand it.

International correlation of the Cainozoic at present encounters many difficulties, and several different sets of stages are necessarily in use in different regions and for different facies. In western Europe, where Tertiary rocks were first studied in detail, a dozen or more stages are in current use, based mainly on marine sections in France, Belgium, Italy and England. Correlation depends largely on marine lamellibranchs and gastropods but also on echinoids, nummulites and vertebrates. These stages are recognized in some other parts of the world, but elsewhere local schemes are in use. For example, in California the Cainozoic is divided into about a dozen local stages defined and divided into zones on the basis of Foraminifera. There are mostly two zones to a stage, so that in this case subdivision by Foraminifera does not permit the precision sometimes obtainable with, say, ammonoids or trilobites. For the continental facies in North America H. E. Wood and others (1941) proposed eighteen 'ages' (properly stages) defined by land mammals. Correlation of these mammal stages with subdivisions founded on marine sequences is only approximate.

The foregoing review shows that few schemes of classification in fact make use of both series (in the biostratigraphical sense) and stages. In the Mesozoic and Cainozoic division of the system into lower and upper, or lower, middle and upper parts provides subdivision on the same scale as would be provided by series. Estimates of the duration in years of stratigraphical divisions in the palaeozoic (p. 71) shows no significant difference between units called stages in the Carboniferous and Permian and series in the Ordovician and Silurian of Europe.

BIOSTRATIGRAPHICAL AND CHRONOSTRATIGRAPHICAL UNITS

Some workers, including a majority of the International Subcommission on Stratigraphic Terminology (Hedberg 1961) and the formulators of the American Code, have maintained that there is a fundamental distinction between the zone and the higher categories into which zones are grouped. Zones are referred to as biostratigraphical units and the others as time-stratigraphical or chronostratigraphical units. The basis for this distinction is that while zones are defined solely by fossils, 'a chronostratigraphic unit is a body of rock strata which is unified by representing the rocks formed during a specific interval of geologic time ... The boundaries of a chrono-stratigraphic unit, as they are extended away from its type or reference section, are by definition surfaces of equal time value everywhere (isochronous surfaces). In practice, this means that these boundaries are surfaces of equal time value to the limits of the current resolving power of existing geologic methods' (Hedberg 1961, p. 12).

Other workers, including J. A. Jeletzky (1956, p. 699),

C. O. Dunbar and J. Rodgers (1957, p. 293), O. H. Schindewolf (in Hedberg 1961, p. 31), T. G. Miller (1965) and the present writer, disagree with this view. They maintain that the boundaries of 'time-stratigraphical' units can only be fixed on biostratigraphical criteria, and hence have no separate existence. As Teichert has written (1958, p. 116): 'The only practical time-stratigraphic boundaries are interfaces between two superimposed biostratigraphic units, selected in an area where the succession of biostratigraphic units during the critical interval is as complete as possible and from which these units can be traced to other parts of the world.' It is true that, as Arkell pointed out in the quotation given above, 'stages transcend zones', but, considered as time-units, their boundaries are likely to be less good approximations to isochronous surfaces than those of zones.

Relationships between different kinds of stratigraphical units are shown in a diagram devised by C. H. Holland (Fig. 32). Horizontal lines are supposed to be of constant age: they are true 'time-boundaries'. Zones are supposed to provide almost perfect time boundaries, and in the zonal province in which it is defined the stage also has such boundaries. Outside this province correlation is less precise and the stage boundaries diverge appreciably from being isochronous surfaces, but they are the best approximation that we can get. Formations, defined by lithology, have boundaries of variable age.

The position adopted here, then, is that zone, stage, series and system are all units of the same kind: they are biostratigraphical units, which is merely another way of stating that they are defined by fossils.

SUBDIVISION OF GEOLOGICAL TIME

We often need to refer to the time during which a particular set of rocks was formed, or some other geological event took place. We can do this explicitly: we can say that a certain episode of earth-movement in an area occurred 'during the time when the Ashgill Series was being deposited elsewhere'. This is clumsy and most people will be content to say instead 'during Ashgill times', although we do not say 'during the Ashgill Series'. The word 'series' is understood to refer to

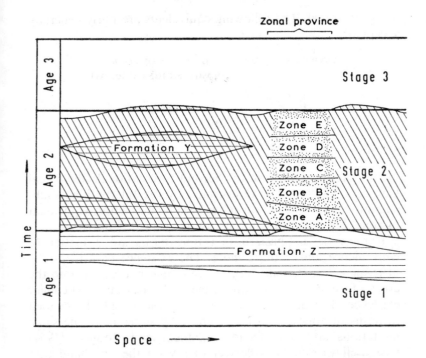

FIG. 32. Relationships between different kinds of stratigraphical units. Horizontal lines are isochronous. Zones A-E (stippled) are supposed to be well-defined biozones and their boundaries are the nearest approximations to isochronous lines that can be obtained. They define Stage 2 (oblique ruling) which has its type area within the zonal province. Outside the zonal province correlation of the stage is less good and its boundaries deviate further from isochronous surfaces. Two formations X and Y (horizontal ruling) are shown which have diachronous boundaries independent of the zone and stage boundaries. Adapted from Holland (1964).

actual rocks and cannot be used in their absence. Similarly we may say 'during Bucklandi times', describing an event which took place during the time marked by the Jurassic zone of that name, and even 'in the Jurassic', although here some noun is understood, the word Jurassic being, strictly speaking, adjectival. Although we can often manage with such devices, it is useful to have terms to express the portions of geological time during which stratigraphical units of various sizes were being deposited. The following equivalents are fairly generally accepted:

DIVISIONS OF TIME	DIVISIONS OF ROCK (biostratigraphical terms)
Era	—
Period	System
Epoch	Series
Age	Stage
—	Zone

These terms date from the Second International Geological Congress, 1881, and were accepted by the International Sub-commission in 1960. *Moment* has been used as a time-equivalent of zone, but is not in common use.

It must be emphasized that time terms are a matter of convenience and nothing more. The existence of a hierarchy of terms—Era, Period, Epoch, Age—must not lead us into the error of supposing that this 'time scale' has an independent existence. The units of time can, at present, only be defined in terms of zones, stages, etc. and they suffer from the same limitations and imperfections. Dunbar and Rodgers (1957) have well written 'it is correct to say on the one hand that certain dinosaurs lived during the Jurassic Period and on the other that their remains are found in the Jurassic System . . . It should be pointed out, however, that the only possible evidence that the dinosaurs lived during the Jurassic Period is precisely that their remains are found in the Jurassic System, so that the first statement actually adds no new information to the second; it merely states the inference instead of the basis for the inference'.

It will be seen from the above that units of geological time must have the same names as the biostratigraphical units to which they correspond. Thus we speak of Ordovician System or Ordovician Period, Albian Stage or Albian Age, according to whether we are referring to the rocks themselves or the time occupied by their accumulation. Then there is no likelihood of confusion.

Several other time terms have been proposed but have never achieved general recognition. Perhaps the most notorious is the *hemera* proposed by S. S. Buckman in 1893. It is a Greek word and Buckman explained that 'Its meaning is "day" or "time" ... Successive hemerae should mark the smallest consecutive divisions which the sequence of different species enables us to separate in the maximum developments of strata. ... The term "hemera" is intended to mark the acme of development of one or more species'. Buckman had realized that the ammonites, with which he was working, could be used to provide very detailed subdivisions for which no suitable term existed. Hemerae were much used by English Jurassic workers for about forty years, but hardly at all by anyone else. One difficulty in using the hemera lay in determining the acme or time of greatest abundance of a species, since this can clearly be affected by facies or by local accidents of preservation, so that although the hemera may be a valid concept it is of little practical value. Other factors also brought it into disrepute. Buckman's later work was characterized by long lists of hemerae which were open to criticism for at least three reasons: first, he indulged in taxonomic 'splitting', so that several hemeral indices might in fact have been variants of one species; second, he seems to have believed that two species never reached their acme simultaneously so that the hemera of each species necessarily marked a distinct time-interval; third, he placed the hemerae in order in his tables according to hypothetical evolutionary sequences (deduced from the theory of biological recapitulation and supposed cycles of evolution) and not from actual collecting.

The term *biochron* was invented by H. S. Williams (1901) for the length of time defined by the range of a fossil species or higher systematic category. By analogy with this W. J. Arkell (1933, p. 33) suggested *teilchron* for the time-unit defined by the local range of a species. These two terms correspond to biozone and teilzone on the biostratigraphical scale (see p. 54). They have not been much used except in discussions of stratigraphical principles.

MAJOR TIME TERMS

We frequently need to differentiate between geological time before the Cambrian, for which correlation by fossils is impossible, and that part beginning with the appearance of abundant

L

fossils at the base of the Cambrian. Pre-Cambrian describes the first part, and has the advantage of being explicit, but for the second part 'post-Pre-Cambrian' and 'Cambrian and later' are both too clumsy. The terms Cryptozoic ('hidden life') and Phanerozoic ('evident life') were suggested by G. H. Chadwick in 1930 and seem to be gaining general acceptance.

The Cryptozoic has not been divided into periods of world-wide validity because of the impossibility, until recently, of correlation between different areas. Local systems have been used in each area, delimited by unconformities, differences in metamorphic grade or even by tectonic contacts such as thrust planes. Now that correlation by radiometric dating is in sight, universal subdivisions of the Cryptozoic may in due course be established, perhaps when suitable events have been recognized corresponding to the palaeontological events by which Phanerozoic systems are defined.

The three eras of the Phanerozoic—Palaeozoic, Mesozoic and Cainozoic—were suggested by William Smith's nephew John Phillips in 1840. We now know that the Palaeozoic was longer than the Mesozoic and Cainozoic combined, and so it is divided into Older Palaeozoic and Younger Palaeozoic. The terms Proterozoic and Deuterozoic were used for these two divisions in England towards the end of the nineteenth century, but did not find general acceptance. Proterozoic was also used as a subdivision of Cryptozoic in North America at about the same time (p. 98). The boundaries between the eras are discussed in the next chapter.

RUSSIAN PRACTICE

Current practice in the USSR differs from that in western Europe and America, in that it does not recognize two parallel scales, one lithostratigraphical and one biostratigraphical. Instead, the biostratigraphical scale is used down to as small a subdivision as possible in any particular case, and then a local scale takes over.

Procedure and terminology were worked out by a Stratigraphic Commission set up in 1952, and the results have been published in English (Rotay 1960). The need for a single, universal scale is emphasized; this is, of course, the biostratigraphical scale of Western geologists but is termed the unique stratigraphical scale. Corresponding time terms are recognized:

Stratigraphical subdivisions	Geochronological subdivisions
Gruppa (Group)	Era
Sistema (System)	Period
Otdel (Section)	Epokha (Epoch)
Yarus (Stage)	Vek (Age)
Zona (Zone)	Vremya (Time)

As far as possible, rocks are to be classified in the unique subdivisions, but local subdivisions are permitted where rocks cannot be correlated closely with the unique scale, or for specific purposes such as geological mapping. The auxiliary scale for local use is:

Serya (Series)
Svita (Suite)
Pachka (Packet)

These local units will often be lithostratigraphical but they may also be biostratigraphical, for example where fossils available for local subdivision cannot be correlated with the faunas used for defining the unique scale. The Russians deny the distinction, merely stating that subdivisions are to be defined by all their characters, lithological and palaeontological.

For a particular region . . . 'The tying up of the "unique" scale and the "auxiliary" subdivisions . . . will be achieved by subordinating the auxiliary unit that is highest in rank of those used in the given case to the smallest possible subdivision of the unique scale . . .' for example:

Unique {
 Group
 System
 Section
 Stage
}
Auxiliary {
 Suite
 Packet
}

or

Unique {
 Group
 System
}
Auxiliary {
 Series
 Suite
 Packet
}

Examples adapted from British and American stratigraphy might be, using Russian terms:

	(Group) Mesozoic			(Group) Palaeozoic
Unique	(System) Jurassic	Unique		(System) Permian
	(Section) Middle Jurassic			(Stage) Guadalupian
Auxiliary	(Suite) Deltaic Series	Auxiliary	(Suite) Carlsbad
	(Packet) Scarborough Beds		Limestone

Practice among English-speaking geologists goes some way towards the Russian ideal in that rock-stratigraphical units are not used in the higher ranks, as pointed out earlier in this chapter. It differs in the conscious use, in some cases, of a biostratigraphical scale alongside rock units in order to examine the relationships of the latter to time. Presumably such an examination cannot conveniently be made in the USSR, unless auxiliary units are used alongside the unique scale. The general impression given by the Russian exposition of principles is that widespread diachronism of rock-units is not apprehended, and that there is a tendency to assume that lithological boundaries are the reflection of general causes, and are thus isochronous (see also p. 182). The need for a dual classification does not, perhaps, seem so necessary to the Russian stratigrapher as to his European or American counterpart. Apart from this limitation, the Russian scheme has its points. Illogical as it may seem at first sight to combine universal and local subdivisions into one classification, we do this when we arrange local rock-units into systems, and plenty of examples of the mixture of two kinds of unit (intentional or otherwise) occur in Western literature. It was the standard practice of the United States Geological Survey in the earlier part of the present century (Willmarth 1925).

8

GEOLOGICAL BOUNDARIES

BOUNDARIES between formations are usually defined on lithological grounds, and some of the problems of fixing them have been mentioned in Chapter 1. It is desirable that they be convenient for mapping, and in poorly exposed regions they will tend to lie at major changes of lithology which can be traced by means of soil or relief. Where lithology changes gradually the boundary must be arbitrary. In such cases one can sometimes use a distinctive bed, as in the Kimmeridge Clay —Portland Beds junction in Dorset (p. 23), or the earliest appearance of a particular rock-type. Thus the Old Red Sandstone–Lower Limestone Shale boundary in Somerset is placed at the lowest bed of limestone. Disputes about formation boundaries are seldom of more than local importance.

Zones have been discussed in Chapter 2. Their lower boundaries are marked by the appearance in the succession of the characteristic fossil or fossils, the upper boundary usually by the entry of the fauna characteristic of the succeeding zone. In the ideal case, of a biozone of which the index species is a member of an evolving lineage, there is in theory the difficulty of fixing a line in a gradually changing series of forms. In practice this is often resolved by the existence of unfossiliferous beds, or a non-sequence, or perhaps a local absence of the species in question, which produces a discontinuity in the lineage which can be taken as a zonal boundary. Where the diagnostic event is the migration of a species or fauna into the zonal province there is seldom difficulty in deciding on the boundary.

There have often been differences in local usage of zonal schemes, but by and large stratigraphers have striven for uniformity. In many cases a particular area has, by common consent, been regarded as providing a standard which workers in other areas have tried to follow. Examples that come to mind are the Ardennes, the Eifel and neighbouring areas for the Devonian goniatite zones and Scandinavia for the Upper Cambrian trilobite zones of Europe. These areas often have a more complete or more fossiliferous succession than elsewhere.

Major boundary problems arise when we come to define larger biostratigraphical units such as stages or systems, which should be of world-wide validity. In these cases, with great variety of lithological and faunal developments, as well as differences of local opinion, the difficulty of arriving at universally agreed boundaries is greatest.

STAGE BOUNDARIES

Lack of agreement as to the stages to be used and the boundaries between them is one of the major difficulties in stratigraphy at the present time. Disagreements exist as to some of the system boundaries, as will be shown, but the cases here are few enough to be easily kept in mind and while they are regrettable they do not often mislead. But when we come to consider stages we find differing usages and controversy in almost every system. I am not here speaking of local variations and difficulties caused by facies, faunal provinces and so on, but of disagreement as to the units to be used and their boundaries when the correlation itself is not in dispute. One example will suffice, that of the Toarcian-Bajocian boundary with the possible insertion of the Aalenian Stage in between (Fig. 33).

The original Jurassic stages of d'Orbigny are given on page 156. The Toarcian was proposed for rocks then called Upper Lias by English and French geologists and the Bajocian for rocks called Inferior Oolite. Zonal stratigraphy was non-existent. The first indication of the boundary between the two stages was given by d'Orbigny in lists of characteristic fossils of each published in 1850. Critical species are *Ammonites opalinus* and *Am. torulosus*, included in Toarcian, and *Am. murchisonae*, *Am. sauzei* and *Am. sowerbyi* listed for Bajocian. All these species were later used as zonal indices. The table for the relevant part of the succession is:

MODERN ZONES	OPPEL'S ZONES, 1856	
	(higher zones of Bajocian)	

Stephanoceras humphriesianum — Am. humphriesianus

Otoites sauzei — Am. sauzei

Sonninia sowerbyi — Am. sowerbyi ⎫ Original

Graphoceras concavum ⎫ — Am. murchisonae ⎬ Aalenian

Ludwigia murchisonae ⎭ — ⎬ Stage of

Tmetoceras scissum ⎫ ⎰ Trigonia navis ⎭ Mayer-Eymar

Leioceras opalinum ⎭ ⎱ Am. torulosus ⎭

Dumortieria levesquei ⎫

Grammoceras thouarsense ⎬ Am. jurensis

Haugia variabilis ⎭

(lower zones of Toarcian)

Interpreting d'Orbigny's lists in terms of the modern zonal succession, the Opalinum Zone goes into the Toarcian and the Murchisonae Zone into the Bajocian.

Two years later d'Orbigny described the stages more fully (1852), and defined each in three ways. First, stratigraphical position (i.e. the Bajocian lies above the Toarcian and below the Bathonian); second, fauna; third, formations described by previous workers which he included in the stage. The first seldom contributes to the precise definition of the stage, and we are left with the second and third criteria. The second corresponds with the hierarchical method of definition (p. 145) since in practice the stage is taken to include the zones in which the fossils specified by d'Orbigny are now known to occur. The third constitutes a typological definition. Not surprisingly we now find contradictions between d'Orbigny's definitions, because he did not realize that the faunal succession could be divided into zones and that in fact the faunas replaced one another gradually and not suddenly.

In the sections in the Toarcian and Bajocian Stages described in 1852 (pp. 463–491) the boundary between the stages was placed at different levels in different places, later found to range from the base of the Opalinum Zone near Thouars (Deux-Sèvres) to a line within the Murchisonae Zone at La Verpillière (Isère). Albert Oppel, the first to provide zonal subdivision for the Jurassic (1856–1858), adopted the lower of these boundaries on the grounds that Thouars (Lat. *Toarcium*) was the type locality of the Toarcian. This was lower than the boundary indicated by the original faunal lists. Oppel also regarded this line as the natural boundary between Lower and Middle Jurassic, the ammonites which enter in the Opalinum Zone being the first members of the Graphoceratidae, an important Bajocian family.

A surprisingly different conclusion emerged from a study of what is claimed to be the type-section of the Bajocian by M. Rioult (1964). The stage was named from Bayeux (Lat. *Bajoce*) in Calvados, Normandy and d'Orbigny mentioned a number of places where it was exposed. The choice of a type-section is limited by the fact that the inland sections are now obscured and only the coastal exposures survive. There, according to Rioult, d'Orbigny indicated a lithological junction between green beds (below) and rusty-coloured beds (above), corresponding to the Toarcian-Bajocian boundary. Later collecting has shown this boundary to lie between the Sauzei and Humphriesianum Zones, much higher than any author has ever taken it!

A further complication was introduced with the proposal of the Aalenian Stage by C. D. W. Mayer-Eymar in 1864. The name derives from Aalen (Württemberg, Germany) and the stage originally comprised Oppel's Torulosus to Sowerbyi Zones inclusive. Ten years later Mayer-Eymar moved the upper boundary of the Aalenian down a zone to the base of the Sowerbyi Zone. Mayer-Eymar appears to have been a nonentity who was preoccupied with schemes of classification, but the Aalenian was given wide currency by the eminent French stratigrapher Emile Haug who adopted it in his text-book (1910), altering its lower boundary, however, to include the Levesquei Zone. Mayer-Eymar and Haug restricted the Bajocian to that part of the original stage lying above the Aalenian. The Aalenian happens to form a conspicuous lithological unit, sedimentary iron ore with abundant ammonites, in north-eastern France and was adopted by many French workers.

To summarize, d'Orbigny provided several contradictory definitions of the Toarcian-Bajocian boundary and two of them, below and above Opalinum Zone, have each been widely adopted. Others who accept the Aalenian, employ a restricted Bajocian above it. Moreover the Lower-Middle Jurassic boundary is taken by some below the Aalenian, by others above it (Fig. 33). There is thus great confusion and one must ascertain in each case the meaning which an author attaches to the terms he uses. Recent differences of opinion are largely between British and French. British authors advocate adherence to Oppel's boundary on the grounds that he was the first worker to interpret d'Orbigny's definitions in terms

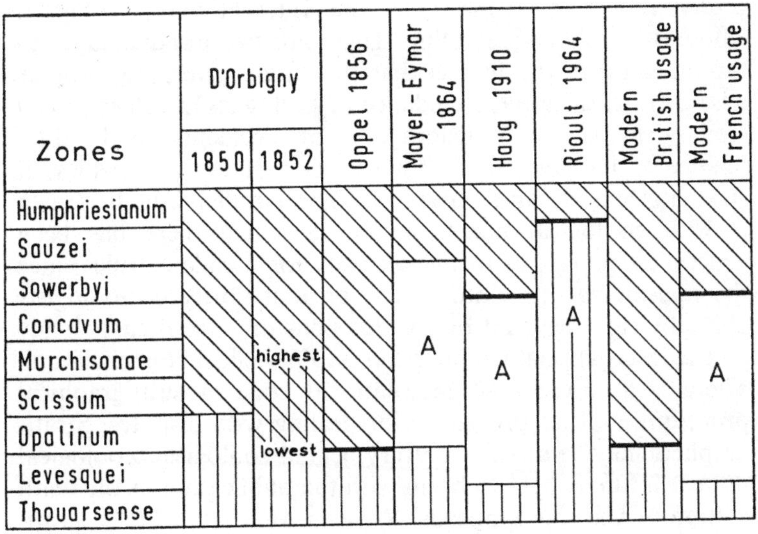

FIG. 33. Some interpretations of the Toarcian-Bajocian boundary. Vertical ruling = Toarcian Stage, diagonal ruling = Bajocian Stage, A = Aalenian Stage. Thick lines show the position of the Lower-Middle Jurassic boundary. Mayer-Eymar (1864) placed this boundary at the base of the Toarcian Stage. Haug (1910) did not recognize Lower and Middle Jurassic but placed the division between his Liassic and Oolitic Sub-Systems at the top of the Aalenian Stage. Rioult regarded the Aalenian as a substage of the Toarcian.

of the zonal succession. They reject Aalenian and place the Toarcian-Bajocian boundary between the Levesquei and Opalinum Zones. The French, on the other hand, are understandably loth to abandon the Aalenian Stage which has been in current use for half a century, although unfortunately in a confusing variety of interpretations. There is no sign at present of either side being willing to give in to the other.

Many other stage boundaries are in dispute after the fashion recorded above. It is one of the urgent tasks of stratigraphy to seek international agreement in these cases, as far as is consistent with the correlations which can be made. Since the war some progress has been made by colloquia of specialists. The best solution is clearly for workers in a particular system to reach agreement among themslves. If they cannot, then presumably a body such as the International Geological Congress may make a ruling. There are two disadvantages to this procedure: the first is that the ruling given may not be wise or just, since the attendance of geologists at International Congresses is partly determined by accidents of locality, finance and so on; and second, such a ruling is worthless if stratigraphers do not observe it. The parallel usually drawn is with zoological nomenclature, in which there has been general agreement as to the necessity for a code of rules since the mid-nineteenth century. The great majority of zoologists abide by the rules and by the decisions on special cases made by the International Commission on Zoological Nomenclature. There is at present no international code of stratigraphical procedure and no procedure for dealing with disputes. Stratigraphers may be about a century behind zoologists. Zoological nomenclature is held to begin with the publication of the tenth edition of Carolus Linnaeus' *Systema Naturae* in 1758; stratigraphical stages and zones originated in the mid-nineteenth century, while the idea of a set of rules to govern interpretation and nomenclature has only come into prominence recently.

SYSTEM BOUNDARIES

The approximate limits of the systems are usually determined for us by original definition or by usage. We could not, even if we so wished, make major changes to them. Within certain limits, however, many boundaries are in dispute, either because of long-standing differences of opinion between different workers (usually in different countries), or as a result of new discoveries which compel reconsideration of previous ideas. There has in addition been much discussion as to the criteria which should be given most weight. This may be illustrated by accounts of actual cases, followed by a summary of views.

THE CAMBRIAN–ORDOVICIAN BOUNDARY

North Wales	Öland
Arenig Series	Megalaspis limestones
—unconformity—	
Tremadoc Slates	⎧ Ceratopyge and Apatokephalus beds ⎨ Dictyonema Shale ⎩ Obolus Conglomerate
Dolgelley Beds	Stinkstones or sandstones

It is reasonable to turn first to North Wales where the Cambrian was defined by Sedgwick (1835). Sedgwick also included the Arenig Series in his Cambrian but it was later removed, first into 'Lower Silurian' and later, with the foundation of the Ordovician System by Lapworth in 1879, into that system. The Tremadoc Slates were retained in the Cambrian, the dividing line being selected by Lapworth on the grounds of the faunal change between the Tremadoc and the Arenig. The unconformity at the base of the Arenig was convenient for mapping so this boundary was adopted by the Geological Survey of Great Britain and is still used by them.

In Scandinavia the situation is different. In the Baltic island of Öland and elsewhere beds correlated with the Tremadoc Slates of Wales form, with the equivalents of the earliest Arenig rocks, a condensed series of limestones and shales with many small discontinuities, but no break at the level where Tremadoc faunas give place to Arenig ones. The only conspicuous break is marked by the base of the Obolus Conglomerate, and in some parts of Sweden where the conglomerate is absent there is a stratigraphic gap below the Dictyonema Shale. Scandinavian geologists place the base of the Ordovician at the base of the Obolus Conglomerate or (where it is absent) of the Dictyonema Shale, and their practice is supported by study of the graptolite faunas. The earliest graptolites are found in the Tremadoc Slates and in the Dictyonema Shales, and as graptolites are used for zoning throughout the Ordovician their first appearance is held by many to be an appropriate level for the base of the system. Furthermore, the trilobite fauna of the Tremadoc Slates and their equivalents elsewhere is now thought to be dominantly Ordovician in its affinities, although it can be argued that it is in some respects intermediate between the Cambrian and Ordovician faunas.

We see from the above that historical considerations favour placing the boundary above the Tremadoc; arguments from physical breaks in the succession support different interpretations in different areas; while faunal arguments tend to favour placing the boundary at the base of the Tremadoc. Most geologists, including a number of British workers outside the Geological Survey, now adopt the lower boundary.

THE SILURIAN-DEVONIAN BOUNDARY

The controversy over this boundary is not yet settled, or even in sight of settlement (Fig. 34). The highest rocks originally included in the Silurian were described by R. I. Murchison around Ludlow, in Shropshire, and named by him the Upper Ludlow Rock. The Upper Ludlow is in marine facies but the overlying rocks are the non-marine Old Red Sandstone facies of the Devonian. Murchison found a gradual lithological and faunal transition from the Ludlow into the Old Red Sandstone (1839, pp. 181, 197–198, 602):

O.R.S. { Tilestone, about 150 ft.

Silurian {
passage beds, about 25 ft.
Downton-castle building stone, 12 to 14 ft.
Fish-bed, 8 to 10 ft, with the [Ludlow] bone bed in the middle.

Murchison seems to have included the passage beds in the Silurian but his description is ambiguous on this point.

Both the highest Silurian and the lowest O.R.S. contain invertebrate shells as well as chordates ('fish'), but the former predominate in the Silurian while fish are characteristic of the O.R.S. In the Tilestone Murchison recorded that fish prevail over mollusca and this, together with the presence of red layers, may have caused him to include them in the O.R.S. Some years later, Murchison (1845) came to think that the fossils of the Tilestone were mainly species characteristic of the Upper Ludlow. He therefore moved the upper limit of the Upper Ludlow and of the Silurian to the top of the Tilestone.

Straw (1930) suggested that Murchison was misled regarding the palaeontology of the Tilestone and its equivalents, and if this was so the revision carries little weight and arguments of priority or historical importance would favour the original line.

The Devonian System was proposed by Sedgwick and Murchison (1839) for the rocks between the Silurian and Carboniferous Systems. They included the Old Red Sandstone in the System. The boundary between the Silurian and Devonian Systems is not seen in Devonshire. So far as type areas are concerned, therefore, the only chance of fixing a boundary is around Ludlow, the type-locality of the highest rocks originally defined as Silurian; but here the boundary must be fixed between marine Silurian and non-marine Old Red Sandstone.

During the rest of the nineteenth and in the early twentieth centuries different authors adopted one or the other of Murchison's two alternatives. A third was added when L. D. Stamp in 1920 argued that the boundary should be stabilized in approximately Murchison's original sense, but proposed to place it at the Ludlow Bone Bed as an easily recognizable local horizon. About this time, however, a completely new point of view began to appear.

The Downtonian Stage had been proposed by Charles Lapworth for the beds included by Murchison in his Upper Ludlow. Its meaning later became changed to include the rocks from the Fish Bed to the Tilestone inclusive. W. W. King and W. J. Lewis (1917) raised the upper boundary of this stage to include several hundred feet of beds, and in later papers King further raised the boundary until the Downtonian included over 2,000 feet of strata, the greater part in the red beds facies of the O.R.S. He also proposed in 1921 the Dittonian Stage for a further 750 feet of rocks above the Downtonian. Thus the whole of the Lower Old Red Sandstone was divided between these two stages. This in itself was progressive and the stages have been accepted. In his earlier papers King regarded these stages as transitional between Silurian and Devonian. But finally, in 1934, he included both the Downtonian and Dittonian Stages in the Silurian!

King's reason for doing this was the faunal continuity (in his view) between Ludlow, Downtonian and Dittonian rocks.

No worker seems to have followed him in placing Dittonian in the Silurian, but some have accepted a Silurian–Devonian boundary between Downtonian and Dittonian. Thus there is at present a major disagreement between geologists who place the boundary below the Downtonian and those who place it above.

E. I. White, an authority on the vertebrate fauna of the Old Red Sandstone, in 1950 supported Stamp's proposal. He stressed the arbitrary nature of boundaries, pointing out that faunas evolved gradually and continuously and changes such as the appearance of the Downtonian vertebrate fauna are local accidents. He thought that in view of the difficulty of agreeing on a palaeontological boundary in a gradually changing fauna one should fix boundaries according to historical priority, though he favoured the lowering of Murchison's original boundary to the Ludlow Bone Bed for the sake of local convenience. The drawback to this procedure, in the present case, is that the boundary is fixed on the basis of local lithology and takes no account of the advances in knowledge of the faunal succession since Murchison. White conceded that correlation between the Ludlow area and fully marine successions was unsatisfactory, but thought it would be achieved in due course through areas with alternating marine and non-marine facies.

L. B. H. Tarlo (1964) has argued for the boundary at the top of the Downtonian on faunal grounds. He maintained that the faunal change across the Ludlow Bone Bed is negligible, but that an important change in the vertebrate faunas occurs at the base of a unit called the 'Psammosteus' Limestone Group with the incoming of the genera *Traquairaspis* and *Proteropteraspis*. Tarlo takes this unit to mark the base of the Dittonian Stage and of the Devonian System, and claims that the faunal change can also be recognized in the 'Old Red Sandstone' facies of other regions including Nova Scotia, Spitzbergen and the Ukraine. His reasoning is open to criticism on one point. The appearance of the *Traquairaspis-Proteropteraspis* fauna in the Welsh Borderland coincides with a facies change from subtidal and intertidal to dominantly fluviatile conditions. It could be, therefore, that the fauna is a facies fauna, and while it may be true that these genera did not exist as early as the base of the Downtonian, their actual entry into the sequence may be due to migration consequent upon facies change.

It was for long customary in the fully marine sequence of Bohemia and Thuringia to place the Silurian–Devonian boundary at the level at which the graptolites died out. In these marine areas there are six or eight graptolite zones above the horizon of *Monograptus leintwardinensis*, the highest English graptolite from the lower part of the Upper Ludlow. It is clear that graptolites disappeared from the Welsh Border-

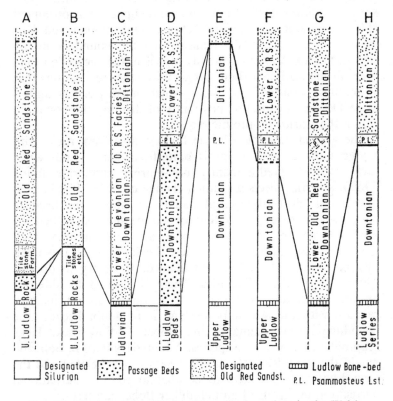

FIG. 34. History of the Silurian-Devonian boundary in the Welsh Borderland. A, Murchison (1839); B, Murchison (1845); C, Stamp (1920); D, King and Lewis (1917); E, King (1934); F, Pocock and Whitehead (1935, fig. 34); G, White (1950); H, Tarlo (1964). Simplified from White (1950).

land with the incoming of non-marine conditions but persisted longer elsewhere, and it has recently been realized that the highest graptolitic beds in central Europe are to be correlated with early Devonian rocks in western Europe and North America. Consequent upon this discovery H. Jaeger in 1962 proposed to take the boundary in the marine sequence at the base of the Zone of *Monograptus uniformis*, a horizon believed to correlate approximately with the base of the 'Psammosteus' Limestone Group of the Old Red Sandstone.

The foregoing account shows that no one in Britain had departed far from Murchison's original boundary until 1934. King's extreme view did not command support but prompted others to adopt a boundary between Downtonian and Dittonian. Meanwhile it was realized that the boundary in use in marine areas was substantially higher in the succession than Murchison's original boundary. With the realization that graptolites persisted into rocks which most workers agreed to be Devonian came the possibility of defining the boundary within the marine graptolitic sequence.

The gradual transition in the Ludlow area from rocks with a predominantly marine invertebrate fossil fauna (Ludlow) to rocks with a predominantly non-marine vertebrate fauna (Downtonian), reflects a gradual change of facies. If it be held that major biostratigraphical boundaries should be fixed in places where there is a continuous marine succession then the Welsh Borderland is an unsuitable place, and one must look at areas far distant from those where the Silurian and Devonian Systems were first studied and defined. If we try to do this we run into other difficulties. There is a good fossiliferous marine succession, well exposed, in Bohemia, but its correlation with the Welsh Borderland is in doubt because the dwindling marine fauna in the Upper Ludlow rocks lacks graptolites and is poor in species. A boundary fixed in Bohemia would therefore leave the Ludlow Series uncorrelated and the term Ludlow might have to be abandoned for international correlation in favour of an unfamiliar Bohemian term.

It remains to be seen whether such a change will be accepted by geologists. The strongest argument for it would perhaps be on the grounds that the higher boundary is more easily recognized in different facies throughout the world than the original line. The historical argument, however, is also a strong one.

The Triassic and Jurassic Systems were first studied in north-west Europe where the upper Trias is in non-marine facies (Keuper). The name Trias derives from the threefold subdivision in Germany, the marine, fossiliferous Muschelkalk being sandwiched between non-marine Bunter below and Keuper above. In England the Lias forming the lowest member of the 'Oolite Formation' (later the Jurassic) was observed to rest on Red Marl, or New Red Sandstone, which was correlated with the Keuper. It was found that the rocks resting on the Keuper both in England and on the continent yielded a similar fossil fauna, distinguished by the presence of the bivalve mollusc *Rhaetavicula* [=*Pteria*] *contorta*, and the base of these beds, marked by an abrupt lithological change as well as the sudden appearance of a fauna, was naturally adopted as the boundary between the almost unfossiliferous New Red or Triassic System and the Lias. It was soon recognized that the beds with *R. contorta* showed a number of faunal differences from the main mass of the Lias above; they lack ammonites, and many of the other molluscs belonged to distinct species which did not range higher. Moreover, as marine fossils from the uppermost alpine Trias became known, British palaeontologists found resemblances between them and the fauna of the *R. contorta* beds, and correlated the latter with the Kössen Beds of the eastern alps and with the St Cassian Beds of Bavaria.

The classification of the St Cassian and Kössen beds was for some time controversial, some geologists believing them to be part of the Trias, and others part of the Lias. During the same period, in the mid-nineteenth century, British geologists were also divided in their opinions. In Germany and Austria, however, opinion was gradually hardening in favour of assigning the Kössen Beds and their equivalents to the Trias, and in 1861 C. W. Gümbel proposed the name Rhaetic, after the Rhätikon area, Switzerland, for these beds, which he regarded as the uppermost part of the Trias. In the same year the English geologist Charles Moore proposed to group the *R. contorta* beds and the overlying White Lias as the Rhaetic Formation although he was non-committal as to its classification. In 1865, however, Lyell placed the Rhaetic in the Upper Trias in conformity with Austrian opinion. This position was adopted by the Geological Survey of Great Britain which has maintained it consistently to this day. Meanwhile in 1864 E. Renevier proposed the Rhaetian Stage for the Rhaetic Formation.

It is difficult to decide whether the Rhaetian fauna as a whole is more like that of the Trias or the Lias, and many workers have thought it transitional in character. The most convincing faunal argument for placing it in the Trias rests on the ammonoids. The main feature of the stage from the point of view of ammonite-stratigraphy is a negative one: the absence of most of the earlier Triassic genera and species. The few genera which do occur were the last survivors of the Triassic fauna, and all persisted from the underlying Norian Stage. They do not survive the end of the stage and are replaced by new genera at the base of the Hettangian Stage. As both the Trias and the Jurassic are zoned by ammonites, it is argued that the place of the Rhaetian is naturally with the Trias.

At the present time stratigraphers in most countries include the Rhaetic in the Trias, but French workers, perhaps influenced by Haug who in his *Traité de Géologie* (1910) argued for the transitional nature of the Rhaetic fauna as a whole, include it in the Jurassic.

This summary has shown that the original 'natural' boundary between Trias and Jurassic was chosen on the basis of an abrupt lithological change. As a result of later work on the fossils a higher boundary was adopted by many geologists, particular weight being given to the cephalopod faunas. The higher boundary is now in use even in countries where the lithological break is the most obvious one, with the exception of France. Most stratigraphers have thus been prepared to abandon a locally well-marked boundary in favour of the uniform adoption of one founded on palaeontological criteria.

There is also a practical argument in favour of the higher boundary. It is well defined by the appearance of the ammonite *Psiloceras planorbis*, which is of nearly world-wide occurrence, with an accompanying molluscan fauna. This stratigraphical level is therefore easily recognizable wherever a fossiliferous succession is present. By contrast the base of the Rhaetian Stage is less well-defined.

GENERAL REMARKS ON SYSTEM BOUNDARIES

These case-histories show that lithological boundaries, although usually the bases on which systems were first defined, are found with increasing knowledge to be only of local importance. Fossil faunas, inadequately understood when sedimentary rocks began to be classified, came to carry increasing weight and as they offered the best hope for general correlation important faunal changes were selected by many workers to define boundaries.

Lithological boundaries themselves are only significant because they mark some geological event—an interval of erosion, resulting in unconformity, in the case of the Tremadoc–Arenig boundary of North Wales; a marine transgression in the case of the Keuper–Rhaetic boundary in north-west Europe. Such criteria may be grouped together as ones dependent upon diastrophism. Abrupt and complete changes in the fossil fauna often result from interruptions in sedimentation due to diastrophic causes, because part of the natural faunal succession is missing. Faunal breaks of this kind suffer from the same limitations as diastrophic effects. The most serious limitation of diastrophism is that it is usually more or less local. Although some orogenies affected many parts of the globe, detailed study usually shows that they were made up of a number of phases; some phases were well developed in some areas, others in other areas. Boundaries founded on diastrophism are often convenient within a limited area, but inconvenient for general correlation.

Gaps in the fossil record, due to interrupted sedimentation, may likewise be locally useful for defining boundaries, but as research goes forward successions will often be found which contain the missing part of the faunal sequence. The stage is then set for a controversy as to whether the newly discovered beds should be classified with the beds above the break, or with those below it. This has happened in the case of the

Cretaceous–Paleogene boundary. At localities in western Europe where these rocks were first studied in detail, there is a striking faunal change as well as a sharp physical break between the Chalk, the topmost formation of the Cretaceous, and the beds which rest on it. It is an easy matter to distinguish a late Cretaceous rock from an early Eocene one. Later, beds in chalky facies higher than those originally included in the Chalk were found in some areas, such as Denmark where the Danian Stage was erected to accommodate them, and beds earlier than those originally regarded as the base of the Eocene were found in France and Belgium and named Paleocene. Furthermore, in other countries such as North America and North Africa there were found more or less continuous successions from the Cretaceous into the Tertiary. Disagreements arose as to where the boundary should be drawn in these fuller successions. Although no world-wide diastrophic event can be traced, a sudden world-wide change in fauna has been claimed to occur. This problem will be discussed at the end of this chapter.

Reasons for regarding changes due to evolution as everywhere contemporaneous have been presented in Chapter 2. Palaeontological changes are more often gradual than sudden, at least when a sufficiently complete succession can be studied. Even so, faunal changes offer the best hope of defining boundaries which at least will be recognizable wherever the appropriate fossils occur. Thus the first appearance of the graptolites and the beginning of the Jurassic radiation of the ammonites offer good criteria by which to fix the bases of the Ordovician and of the Jurassic.

Although such criteria may be used (and they are not available for all systems) system boundaries must be precisely defined in terms of stages and ultimately of zones, according to the hierarchical method as explained in the last chapter. In spite of this the foregoing examples show that discussion has often proceeded on two levels simultaneously. In the case of the Silurian and Devonian, authors such as Stamp and White have argued for a typologically defined boundary at an easily recognizable level (the Ludlow Bone Bed) in the Welsh Borderland, while others have discussed the position of the boundary in terms of the zonal sequence in Bohemia, a hierarchical approach. Such inconsistencies affect other boundaries as well, but the problem of fixing a boundary in a local succession, which may be poorly fossiliferous or in a facies which is difficult to correlate, must not be confused with the problem of defining the boundary for the purpose of world-wide correlation. This should be done in terms of a well-known zonal sequence founded on good fossiliferous sections. There is general agreement that such a succession should be marine. Apart from this the choice may be dictated by historical factors or by ease of correlation with other areas, a sequence which can readily be correlated being naturally preferred.

THEORIES OF DIASTROPHISM AND GEOLOGICAL BOUNDARIES

A will o' the wisp that has been pursued by many geologists is the idea that certain diastrophic events were simultaneous and world-wide in their effects and roughly evenly spaced in time. If so, they should provide a convenient way of subdividing geological time. Such a theory was put forward in 1898 by the American T. C. Chamberlin who believed that periodic orogenies resulted from periodic build-up of stress in the crust due to shrinkage of the interior of the earth, followed by general relief of stress resulting in earth-movements when the limit of strength of the crust was reached. Between orogenies sea level would rise due to silting up of ocean basins and other causes; during orogenies sea level would fall as a result of sinking of the ocean floors as shrinkage of the earth continued. Thus the periodicity of diastrophism was reflected in the stratigraphical record. It was also said to be reflected in the palaeontological record, for the recession of the sea from the continental shelves forced the fauna of the shelves into the small remaining areas of shallow water, resulting in severe competition so that 'the destruction of the larger part is inevitable, and the residue is forced to undergo repressive evolution to meet the severe conditions of the new environment'. A different cause of periodicity was suggested in 1924 by J. Joly of Dublin who invoked the steady build-up of heat from radioactive processes, until parts of the crust became molten and diastrophism was facilitated. Joly calculated that this should happen at intervals of from 30,000,000 to 50,000,000 years.

Chamberlin's belief that faunal changes—extinction and evolution—are correlated with physical changes such as orogenies, transgressions and so on has been held by many other geologists. The American pioneer geologist James Hall wrote in 1855: 'I prefer to make the limits where both physical and zoological characters mark the horizon for I am satisfied that it is the natural true view of the matter.' Like the idea of universal orogenies, this idea has been more prominent as a hypothesis than in its actual contributions to boundary problems: it seems seldom that the faunal and physical changes exactly coincide. The sudden extinction of dinosaurs and ammonites nearly coincided with the physical changes at the Cretaceous–Paleocene boundary, discussed below. The near-extinction of ammonoids at the end of the Norian Stage of the Trias just preceded the marine transgression which occurred in many parts of the world in the succeeding Rhaetian Stage.

Chamberlin's ideas were found convincing at the time and were widely accepted in the earlier part of the present century. They still have their supporters. Such a theory, however, depends on a hypothesis of the structure and history of the earth's interior which can provide regular crises. History shows that numerous hypotheses have been put forward, some have been held more or less widely for a time, and most have been abandoned in due course. There is still no generally accepted theory of earth structure which provides a convincing basis for regular, world-wide diastrophism, nor any agreement that diastrophism does, in fact, show such regularity.

Ideas similar to those expounded by Chamberlin, but now generally abandoned in the West, still form part of the Russian philosophy of stratigraphical classification, and run through the recent statement of principles (Rotay 1960). For example, it is there stated that

'The clearest . . . expression of this periodicity appears to be the alternation of long-continued steps of slow and gradual evolutionary development and relatively more short-lived steps of significantly more rapid qualitative transformation in the face of the earth, at a time during which took place a great rearrangement of the internal structure of the earth's crust . . .'

It is implied that the short-lived steps of rapid change were simultaneous everywhere and thus afford a sound basis for defining boundaries. 'Each of the subdivisions of the stratigraphic scale should correspond to a definite natural-historical stage in the general evolution of the Earth, and above all in the evolution of the organic world.' The Russians believe that 'stratigraphic classification . . . should aim at the objective differentiation of the geologic history'. (Russian statement in Hedberg 1961, p. 31.) Opposed to this theory is the view that stratigraphical boundaries are in the last resort arbitrary, which is gaining acceptance in the West and is discussed at the end of the chapter. Even if a fundamental periodicity of events in the interior of the earth, whether due to convection currents in the mantle or otherwise, is one day accepted, stratigraphy is unlikely to benefit very much. The crustal expression of such periodicity is complex and takes the form of a large number of small movements, different in different places on account of the great local variation in structure and relief of the crust. Moreover the actual movements, which result from the accumulation of stress locally until the crust gives way, are unlikely to be contemporaneous in different regions. To say this is only to predict from theory what we find in practice. Dating of local earth-movements by biostratigraphical means shows a complex pattern, and single easily-recognizable world-wide events cannot be recognized.

The value of diastrophic criteria for defining major boundaries was long ago demolished in scathing terms by Charles Lapworth (1879):

'To the field geologist . . . who desires . . . an unmistakable base-line for his system, capable of being rigidly defined upon his maps and sections, the presence of a decided unconformability affords the very thing of which he stands most in need. The grouping founded upon stratigraphical breaks commends itself to his mind with a force that is practically irresistible. But it is far otherwise with the cautious systematist, who endeavours to found his systems in accordance with those of Nature herself, upon principles, not of local, but of universal

application. Though fully cognizant of the value of an unconformability as affording him a fairly reliable horizon within
a limited area, he soon learns that it is of all things most
untrustworthy when it extends over regions of large diameter.
It is at most a local phenomenon, wholly misleading except in
local application.

'It is surely a work of supererogation in these days to point
out how the tendency of the entire course of geological discovery
for the last fifty years has been to reduce to a mere shadow the
magnitude of the miraculous and world-wide stratigraphical
breaks that bounded the geologic systems of our forefathers.
The doctrine of universal convulsion and the simultaneous
destruction of all the life upon the earth at the end of each
great epoch has so long since passed into the limbo of exploded
hypotheses, that it would be highly amusing, were it not so
painful, to see its degenerate and impoverished survival—the
dogma of the necessity for general stratigraphical and palaeontological breaks between our modern systems—dragging out
its miserable and ridiculous existence, even in our midst, and
claiming allegiance from men of standing in the science.'

BOUNDARIES OF THE PHANEROZOIC ERAS

John Phillips' familiar division into Palaeozoic, Mesozoic and
Cainozoic is universally accepted because it was founded on
two great faunal changes. The boundary between Palaeozoic and
Mesozoic has been studied by the German palaeontologist O. H.
Schindewolf who has tabulated the ranges of a number of animal
groups, mostly orders, suborders or superfamilies (Fig. 35).
Twenty-one groups, in eight phyla, became extinct almost
simultaneously in the late Permian. Sixteen groups appear
simultaneously as the others disappear, and eight more new
groups first appear during the Trias. Study of a particular
group in more detail gives similar results. Figure 36 shows
partial ranges of a number of superfamilies of Archaeogastropoda. There is a noticeable concentration of extinctions near
the Permo–Trias boundary, and two (possibly three) new
groups appear in the Trias.

These changes must be seen in the context of the larger
number of groups, not included in Figures 35 and 36, which

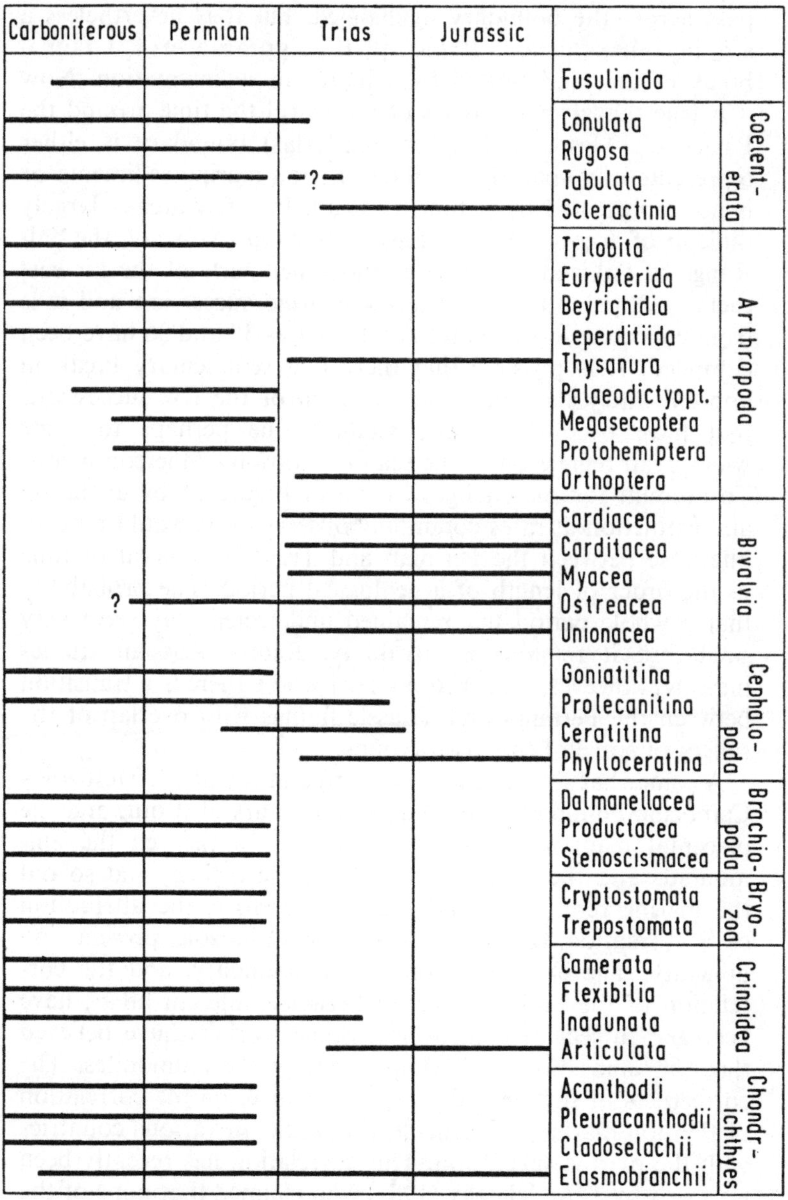

Carboniferous	Permian	Trias	Jurassic		
				Fusulinida	
		—?—		Conulata Rugosa Tabulata Scleractinia	Coelent-erata
				Trilobita Eurypterida Beyrichiida Leperditiida Thysanura Palaeodictyopt. Megasecoptera Protohemiptera Orthoptera	Arthropoda
?				Cardiacea Carditacea Myacea Ostreacea Unionacea	Bivalvia
				Goniatitina Prolecanitina Ceratitina Phylloceratina	Cephalo-poda
				Dalmanellacea Productacea Stenoscismacea	Brachio-poda
				Cryptostomata Trepostomata	Bryo-zoa
				Camerata Flexibilia Inadunata Articulata	Crinoidea
				Acanthodii Pleuracanthodii Cladoselachii Elasmobranchii	Chondr-ichthyes

FIG. 35. Ranges of selected animal groups between the Carboniferous and Jurassic Systems. Modified from Schindewolf (1963).

M

pass across the boundary unchanged, but it is nevertheless a striking phenomenon. It has all the appearance of a faunal break of the kind caused by a hiatus in sedimentation. Now it is true that in many parts of the world the time around the Palaeozoic–Mesozoic (or Permian–Trias) boundary is either represented by sparsely fossiliferous non-marine sediments or is not represented by sediments at all. In a few areas—largely difficult of access—such as East Greenland, Armenia, the Salt Range of Pakistan, Indonesia, and other parts of the far east there is apparently a continuous marine succession and it is from collecting in these areas that Figures 35 and 36 have been compiled. It is possible that there is a sedimentary break in approximately the same place in each of the few successions that have been thoroughly studied, due perhaps to some widespread regression of the sea or elevation of the continents. To account for the changes shown in Figure 35 by evolution and extinction at rates commonly observed one would need to interpose between the Permian and Trias an interval of time of the order of length of a geological period. The probability that a whole period has remained undetected may seem very small but it remains a possibility. Recent Russian studies indicate, however, that sections exist where there is a transition between the Permian and Triassic faunas with overlap of the ranges of some of the fossil groups.

A somewhat similar change occurred at about the Mesozoic–Cainozoic boundary. On land the dinosaurs died out, and the placental mammals suddenly appeared. In the sea the ammonoids and the true belemnites became extinct, and so did the marine reptiles. In most cases, therefore, the attribution of a formation to the Mesozoic or Cainozoic presents no difficulty. The exact position of the boundary, and the correlation of the rocks concerned between different areas, have been the subject of controversy. Some workers have believed that the dinosaurs survived longer than the ammonites. The correctness of this view depends, of course, on the correlation of the non-marine dinosaur-bearing rocks in various countries with the marine succession. This correlation has recently been reviewed by J. A. Jeletzky (1962) who claimed that none of the dinosaur-bearing formations are younger than the Maestrichtian, the stage in which the last ammonites are found. Jeletzky maintains, therefore, that the extinction of the dinosaurs and the ammonites was, geologically speaking, contemporaneous, and forms the natural dividing line between Mesozoic and Cainozoic.

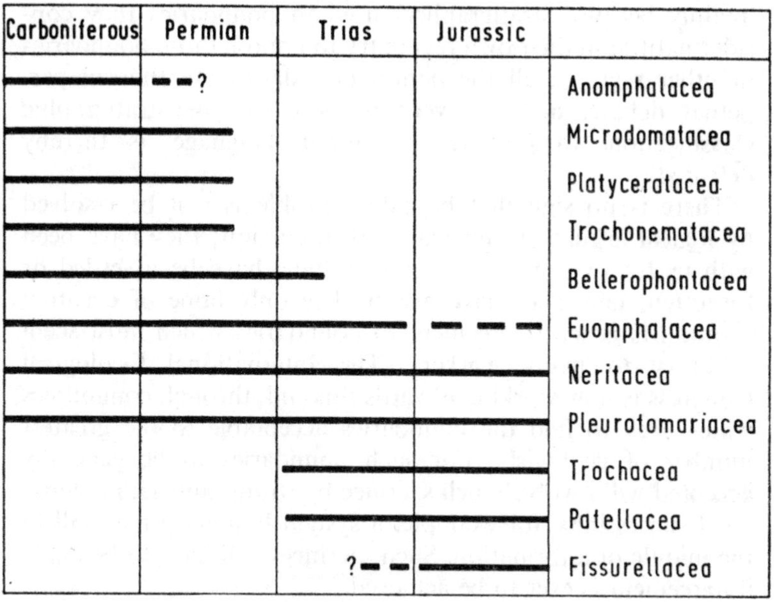

Carboniferous	Permian	Trias	Jurassic	
	— — ?			Anomphalacea
				Microdomatacea
				Platyceratacea
				Trochonematacea
				Bellerophontacea
			— — —	Euomphalacea
				Neritacea
				Pleurotomariacea
				Trochacea
				Patellacea
		? — —		Fissurellacea

Fig. 36. Ranges of certain superfamilies of Archaeogastropoda between the Carboniferous and the Jurassic Systems. Three superfamilies died out before the Carboniferous and one arose after the Jurassic. From information in *Treatise on Invertebrate Paleontology*, Part I, Mollusca 1, 1960.

CONCLUSIONS

The cynical but realistic conclusion to be drawn from these examples is that classification into systems is a matter of convenience; occasionally there may be a well-defined palae-ontological event to define a boundary, but more often there is a choice of several events which were not simultaneous. Diastrophism is seldom found to be of more than local impor-tance, its effects being of different ages in different places. Dunbar and Rodgers (1957) have written: '... the larger units and their boundaries were created in England and western

Europe, and . . . are reasonably natural lithologic and diastrophic units in their type areas, but it is not at all necessary
that they be natural units of that kind for America and
Australia. Their purpose is to provide a common language . . .'.
Disagreements arise, Dunbar and Rodgers go on to say
'mainly because stratigraphers used to boundaries they consider natural in their own region try to impose those boundaries
in other regions; all the period boundaries are thus in per-
petual debate, and the very purpose of time-stratigraphic
classification, to provide a common language, is thereby
defeated'.

There is no sign that boundary problems will be resolved
by logical argument and reasoned discussion; they have been
with us for over a century, and if some have been settled or
forgotten, new ones have arisen. The only hope of eventual
solution is general agreement to boundaries which must seem
arbitrary to many workers. The International Geological
Congress is now working towards this end, through committees
which seek to find the boundaries acceptable to the greatest
number of geologists. For such boundaries to be generally
accepted will involve much sacrifice by stratigraphers, in whose
local successions, for example, a system boundary may fall in
the middle of a formation. Such sacrifices will have to be made
if agreement is ever to be achieved.

LIST OF REFERENCES

ABRARD, R. 1925. *Le Lutétien du bassin de Paris*. Angers.

ADAMS, F. D. & others, 1905. Report of the Special Committee for the Lake Superior Region. *Jour. Geol.* vol. 13, pp. 88–104.

AGER, D. V. 1963. Jurassic stages. *Nature, London* vol. 198, pp. 1045–1046.

AMERICAN COMMISSION ON STRATIGRAPHIC NOMENCLATURE, 1961. Code of stratigraphic nomenclature. *Bull. Amer. Ass. Petrol. Geol.* vol. 45, pp. 645–655.

ARKELL, W. J. 1933. *The Jurassic System in Great Britain*. Oxford.

—— 1946. Standard of the European Jurassic. *Bull. Geol. Soc. Amer.* vol. 57, pp. 1–34.

—— 1947. Geology of the country around Weymouth, Swanage, Corfe and Lulworth. *Mem. Geol. Surv. G.B.*

—— 1956. *Jurassic geology of the world*. Edinburgh & London: Oliver & Boyd.

ARKELL, W. J. & DONOVAN, D. T. 1952. The Fuller's Earth of the Cotswolds, and its relation to the Great Oolite. *Quart. Jour. Geol. Soc. Lond.* vol. 107, pp. 227–253.

ARRHENIUS, G. 1947. Orsakerna till den glacigena lerans varvighet; några fysikalisk och kemiska synpunkter. *Geol. Fören. Stockh. Förh.* vol. 69, pp. 261–269.

BANCROFT, B. B. 1929. Some new species of *Cryptolithus* (s.l.) from the Upper Ordovician. *Mem. Manchr. Lit. Phil. Soc.* vol. 73, pp. 67–98.

BARRELL, J. 1917. Rhythms and the measurements of geologic time. *Bull. Geol. Soc. Amer.* vol. 28, pp. 745–904.

BILLINGS, M. P. 1942. *Structural geology*. New York.

BISAT, W. S. 1924. The Carboniferous goniatites of the north of England and their zones. *Proc. Yorks. Geol. Soc.* vol. 20, pp. 40–124.

BOLTWOOD, B. B. 1907. The disintegration products of uranium. *Amer. Jour. Sci.* ser. 4, vol. 23, pp. 77–88.

BRANSON, C. C. (editor), 1962. *Pennsylvanian System in the United States. A symposium*. Amer. Ass. Petrol. Geol., Tulsa, Oklahoma.

BRINKMANN, R. 1929. Statistisch-biostratigraphische Untersuchungen an Mitteljurassischen Ammoniten über Artbegriff und Stammesentwicklung. *Abh. Ges. Wiss. Göttingen, Math.-phys. Kl.*, new ser. vol. 13, no. 3.

BUCKMAN, S. S. 1893. The Bajocian of the Sherborne district. *Quart. Jour. Geol. Soc. Lond.* vol. 49, pp. 479–522.

—— 1902. The term 'Hemera'. *Geol. Mag.* decade 4, vol. 9, pp. 554–557.

BULLERWELL, W. 1964. Geophysical surveys in the borehole *in* The Geological Survey exploratory borehole at Canvey Island, Essex. *Bull. Geol. Surv. G.B.* no. 21, pp. 23–35.

BULMAN, O. M. B. 1958. The sequence of graptolite faunas. *Palaeontology* vol. 1, pp. 159–173.

BULMAN, O. M. B. 1964. Lower Palaeozoic plankton. *Quart. Jour. Geol. Soc. Lond.* vol. 120, pp. 455–476.

CALLOMON, J. H. 1963. The Jurassic ammonite-faunas of East Greenland. *Experientia*, Basel, vol. 19, pp. 289–294.

—— 1964. Notes on the Callovian and Oxfordian Stages. *Comptes Rendus & Mém. Colloque du Jurassique, Luxembourg 1962*, Luxembourg: Institut grand-ducal, pp. 269–291.

CHADWICK, G. H. 1930. Subdivision of geologic time. *Bull. Geol. Soc. Amer.* vol. 41, pp. 47–48.

CHAMBERLIN, T. C. 1898. The ulterior basis of time divisions and the classification of geologic history. *Jour. Geol.* vol. 6, pp. 449–462.

—— 1909. Diastrophism as the ultimate basis of correlation. *Jour. Geol.* vol. 17, pp. 685-693.

CHAMBERLIN, T. C. & SALISBURY, R. D. 1906. *Geology. Earth History.* Vol. 2. London.

DARWIN, C. 1859. *On the origin of species.* London: John Murray.

DAVIES, J. H. & TRUEMAN, A. E. 1927. A revision of the non-marine lamellibranchs of the Coal Measures, and a discussion of their zonal sequence. *Quart. Jour. Geol. Soc. Lond.* vol. 83, pp. 210–257.

DEAN, W. T., DONOVAN, D. T. & HOWARTH, M. K. 1961. The Liassic ammonite zones and subzones of the north-west European province. *Bull. Brit. Mus. (Nat. Hist.): Geology* vol. 4 (no. 10), pp. 435–505.

DE GEER, G. 1940. Geochronologia Suecica: Principles. *Handl. K. Svenska Vetensk.-Akad.* ser. 3, vol. 18, no. 6.

DEISS, C. 1935. Cambrian-Algonkian unconformity in western Montana. *Bull. Geol. Soc. Amer.* vol. 46, pp. 95–124.

DE LA BECHE, H. T. 1834. *Researches in theoretical geology.* London: Charles Knight.

DOLLO, L. 1910. La Paléontologie éthologique. *Bull. Soc. Belge Géol. Pal. Hydr.* vol. 23, pp. 377–421.

D'ORBIGNY, A. 1842–1851. *Paléontologie française. Terrains jurassiques:* vol. 1. Céphalopodes. Paris: Masson.

—— 1850. *Prodrome de paléontologie stratigraphique universelle des animaux mollusques et rayonnés.* Vol. 1. Paris: Masson.

—— 1852. *Cours élémentaire de paléontologie et de géologie stratigraphiques.* Vol. 2, fascicule 2. Paris: Masson.

DUNBAR, C. O. & RODGERS, J. 1957. *Principles of stratigraphy.* New York: John Wiley.

EKMAN, S. 1935. *Tiergeographie des Meeres.* Leipzig.

ELLES, G. L. 1904. Some graptolite zones in the Arenig rocks of Wales. *Geol. Mag.* decade 5, vol. 1, pp. 199–211.

ELLES, G. L. & WOOD, E. M. R. 1906. *A monograph of British graptolites*, part 5. London: Pal. Soc.

—— —— 1913. *Ibid.*, part 9.

FAIRBAIRN, R. A. 1965. The Great Limestone of Weardale [abstract]. Yorks. Geol. Soc., *Circular* no. 253.

FENTON, C. L. & FENTON, M. A. 1928. Ecologic interpretation of some biostratigraphic terms. *Amer. Midland Nat.* vol. 11, pp. 1–40.

GEIKIE, A. 1893. *Textbook of geology*, 3rd edition.

GEORGE, T. N. 1958. Lower Carboniferous palaeogeography of the British Isles. *Proc. Yorks. Geol. Soc.* vol. 31, pp. 227–318.

GILL, J. E. 1955. Precambrian nomenclature in Canada. *Trans. Roy. Soc. Canada* vol. 49, ser. 3, sect. 4, pp. 25–29.

GRABAU, A. W. 1905. Physical characters and history of some New York formations. *Science*, new ser. vol. 22, pp. 528–535.

GRAY, D. A. 1965. The stratigraphical significance of electrical resistivity marker bands in the Cretaceous strata of the Leatherhead (Fetcham Mill) Borehole, Surrey. *Bull. Geol. Surv. G.B.* no. 23, pp. 65–115.

GÜMBEL, C. W. 1861. *Geognostische Beschreibung des bayerischen Alpengebirges und seines Vorlandes.* Gotha.

HALLAM, A. 1960. A sedimentary and faunal study of the Blue Lias of Dorset and Glamorgan. *Phil. Trans. Roy. Soc.* ser. B, vol. 243, pp. 1–44.

HARLAND, W. B., SMITH, A. G. & WILCOCK, B. (editors), 1964. The Phanerozoic time-scale. *Quart. Jour. Geol. Soc. Lond.* vol. 120s.

HAUG, E. 1910. *Traité de Géologie.* Vol. 2, fasc. 2. Paris.

HEDBERG, H. D. (editor), 1961. Stratigraphic classification and terminology. *Rep. XXI Internat. Geol. Congr., Norden, 1960,* part 25. Copenhagen.

HEDE, J. E. 1921. Gottlands silurstratigrafi. *Sverig. Geol. Unders.* ser. C, no. 305.

HENNINGSMOEN, G. 1957. The trilobite family Olenidae with description of Norwegian material and remarks on the Olenid and Tremadocian Series. *Skr. Norsk Vidensk.-Akad. Oslo, Math.-Naturv. Kl.* 1957, no. 1.

HIND, W. 1896. On zonal divisions of the Carboniferous System. *Geol. Mag.* decade 4, vol. 3, pp. 255–261.

HÖGBÖM, A. G. 1889. Relationen mellan kalcium- och magnesiumkarbonat i den hvarfviga mergeln. *Geol. Fören. Stockh. Förh.* vol. 11, pp. 244–245.

HOLLAND, C. H. 1964. Stratigraphical classification. *Science Progress* vol. 52, pp. 439–451.

HOLLINGWORTH, S. E. 1942. The correlation of gypsum-anhydrite deposits and the associated strata in the north of England. *Proc. Geol. Ass.* vol. 53, pp. 141–151.

HOWELL, B. F. & others, 1944. Correlation of the Cambrian formations of North America. *Bull. Geol. Soc. Amer.* vol. 55, pp. 993–1003.

HUDSON, R. G. S. 1926. Lower Carboniferous zonal nomenclature. Report of committee. *Rep. Brit. Ass. Adv. Sci.* (Southampton, 1925), pp. 256–264.

HUTTON, J. 1788. Theory of the earth; or an investigation of the laws observable in the composition, dissolution, and restoration of land upon the globe. *Trans. Roy. Soc. Edin.* vol. 1, pp. 209–304.

HUTTON, J. 1795. *Theory of the earth, with proofs and illustrations.* Edinburgh. 2 vols. [Vol. 3 was published by the Geological Society of London in 1899].

HUXLEY, T. H. 1862. Anniversary address. *Quart. Jour. Geol. Soc. Lond.* vol. 26, pp. xlii–lxiv. [Later reprinted under the title: Geological contemporaneity and persistent forms of life].

JAMESON, R. 1805. *A mineralogical description of the County of Dumfries.* Edinburgh.

JELETZKY, J. A. 1956. Palaeontology, basis of practical geochronology. *Bull. Amer. Ass. Petrol. Geol.* vol. 40, pp. 679–706.

—— 1962. The allegedly Danian dinosaur-bearing rocks of the globe and the problem of the Mesozoic-Cenozoic boundary. *Jour. Paleont.* vol. 36, pp. 1005–1018.

JOLY, J. 1924. *Radioactivity and the surface history of the earth,* being the Halley Lecture delivered on 28th May, 1924. Oxford. [Later expanded into The Surface-history of the earth, Oxford, 1925; 2nd ed. 1930].

JUX, U. 1957. Die Riffe Gotlands und ihre angrenzenden Sedimentationsräume. *Stockholm Contrib. Geol.* vol. 1, no. 4.

KELLAWAY, G. A. & WELCH, F. B. A. 1948. British Regional Geology. Bristol and Gloucester District. *Mem. Geol. Surv. G.B.*

—— —— 1955. Upper Old Red Sandstone and Carboniferous. *Bristol and its adjoining countries* edited by C. M. MacInnes and W. F. Whittard. Bristol: Arrowsmith, pp. 9–23.

KING, P. B. 1949. [Contribution to discussion in] Sedimentary facies in geologic history (C. R. Longwell, chairman). *Mem. Geol. Soc. Amer.* no. 39, pp. 165–171.

KING, W. W. 1921. The geology of Trimpley. *Trans. Worcestershire Nat. Club.* vol. 7, pp. 319–322.

—— 1934. The Downtonian and Dittonian strata of Great Britain and north-western Europe. *Quart. Jour. Geol. Soc. Lond.* vol. 90, pp. 526–570.

—— & LEWIS, W. J. 1917. The Downtonian of south Staffordshire. *Proc. Birmingham Nat. Hist. Phil. Soc.* vol. 14, pp. 90–99.

KORN, H. 1938. Bewegungen, Schichtenaufbau und Sedimentationsgeschwindigkeiten in einer varistischen Mulde nach Studien im thüringisch-fränkischen Unterkarbon und Oberdevon. *Neues Jahrb. Min.* Beil.-Bd. 74, Abt. A, pp. 50–186.

KOROLJUK, I. K. 1960. Subdivision of the Cambrian and pre-Cambrian of Eastern Siberia according to stromatolites. *Rep. XXI Internat. Geol. Congr., Norden, 1960,* part 8, pp. 113–118. Copenhagen.

LANG, W. D. 1924. The Blue Lias of the Devon and Dorset coasts. *Proc. Geol. Ass.* vol. 35, pp. 169–185.

LAPWORTH, C. 1878. The Moffat Series. *Quart. Jour. Geol. Soc. Lond.* vol. 34, pp. 240–346.

—— 1879. On the tripartite classification of the Lower Palaeozoic rocks. *Geol. Mag.* decade 2, vol. 6, pp. 1–15.

—— 1879–1880. On the geological distribution of the Rhabdophora. *Annals & Mag. Nat. Hist.* ser. 5, vol. 3, pp. 245–257, 449–455; vol. 4, pp. 333–341, 423–431; vol. 5, pp. 45–62, 273–285, 359–369; vol. 6, pp. 16–29, 185–207.

LEHMANN, J. G. 1756. *Versuch einer Geschichte von Flötz-Gebürgen.* Berlin.

LONGWELL, C. R. 1949. Sedimentary facies in geologic history. *Mem. Geol. Soc. Amer.* no. 39.

LYELL, C. 1831–1833. *Principles of geology.* London: John Murray. Vol. 1, 1831; vol. 2, 1832; vol. 3, 1833.

—— 1838. *Elements of geology.* London: John Murray.

—— 1865. *Ibid.* 6th edition.

MAGNUSSON, N. H. 1965. The Pre-Cambrian history of Sweden. *Quart. Jour. Geol. Soc. Lond.* vol. 121, pp. 1–30.

MAYER-EYMAR, C. D. W. 1864. *Tableau synchronistique des terrains jurassiques.* Zürich.

McGOWAN, J. A. 1963. Geographical variation in *Limacina helicina* in the North Pacific. *Systematics Ass. Publ.* no. 5, pp. 109–128.

McQUILLIN, R. 1964. Geophysical investigation of seismic shot-holes in the Cheshire Basin. *Bull. Geol. Surv. G.B.* no. 21, pp. 197–203.

MILLER, T. G. 1965. Time in stratigraphy. *Palaeontology* vol. 8, pp. 113–131.

MOORE, C. 1861. On the zones of the Lower Lias and the Avicula contorta Zone. *Quart. Jour. Geol. Soc. Lond.* vol. 17, pp. 483–516.

MOORE, C. A. 1963. *Handbook of subsurface geology.* New York: Harper & Row.

MOORE, R. C. 1949. Meaning of facies. *In* Sedimentary facies in geologic history (C. R. Longwell, chairman). *Mem. Geol. Soc. Amer.* no. 39, pp. 1–34.

MOVIUS, H. L. 1960. Radiocarbon dates and Upper Palaeolithic archaeology in central and western Europe. *Current Anthropology* vol. 1, pp. 355–391.

MURCHISON, R. I. 1839. *The Silurian System.* London: John Murray.

—— 1845. On the palaeozoic deposits of Scandinavia and the Baltic Provinces of Russia. *Quart. Jour. Geol. Soc. Lond.* vol. 1, pp. 467–494.

OPPEL, A. 1856–1858. Die Juraformation Englands, Frankreichs und des südwestlichen Deutschlands. *Jahreshefte Ver. Vaterl. Naturk. Württemberg.* 12 Jahrg. pp. 121–556; 13 Jahrg. pp. 141–396; 14 Jahrg. pp. 129–291. [Also issued with consecutive pagination.]

PHILLIPS, J. 1840. In *Penny Cyclopaedia* vol. 17, pp. 153–154.

PHILLIPS, W. 1818. *A selection of facts from the best authorities, arranged so as to form an outline of the geology of England and Wales.* London: Wm. Phillips. [Contains folding stratigraphical table by Wm. Buckland].

POCOCK, R. W. & WHITEHEAD, T. H. 1935. British Regional Geology: The Welsh Borderland. *Mem. Geol. Surv. G.B.*

POMPECKJ, J. F. 1914. *Die Bedeutung des schwäbischen Jura für die Erdgeschichte.* Stuttgart.

POTTER, P. E. & DESBOROUGH, G. A. 1965. Pre-Pennsylvanian valley and Caseyville (Pennsylvanian) sedimentation in the Illinois Basin. *Illinois State Geol. Surv. Circular* 384.

RASCOE, B. 1962. Regional stratigraphic analysis of Pennsylvanian and Permian rocks in western mid-continent, Colorado, Kansas, Oklahoma, Texas. *Bull Amer. Ass. Petrol. Geol.* vol. 46, pp. 1345–1370.

REUSCH, H. H. 1883. *Die fossilienführenden krystallinischen Schiefer von Bergen in Norwegen.* (Authorized German translation by R. Baldauf). Leipzig. [For an English summary see *Geol. Mag.* decade 3, vol. 1, pp. 85–91, 1884].

REYNOLDS, S. H. 1926. Progress in the study of the Lower Carboniferous (Avonian) rocks of England and Wales. *Rep. Brit. Ass. Adv. Sci.* (Oxford, 1926), pp. 65–101.

RICHTER-BERNBURG, G. 1964. Solar cycle and other climatic periods in varvitic evaporites. *Problems in palaeoclimatology* edited by A. E. M. Nairn. London: Interscience, pp. 510–521.

RIOULT, M. 1964. Le stratotype de Bajocien. *Comptes Rendus & Mém. Colloque du Jurassique, Luxembourg* 1962. Luxembourg: Institut grand-ducal, pp. 239–258.

ROTAY, A. P. (editor), 1960. *Stratigraphic classification and terminology* [English translation of the second revised edition]. Moscow: State Publishing Office of Scientific and Technical Literature in Geology.

RUBEY, W. W. 1931. Lithologic studies of fine-grained Upper Cretaceous sedimentary rocks of the Black Hills region. *Prof. Paper U.S. Geol. Surv.* 165-A, pp. 1–54.

SCHENCK, H. G. & MULLER, S. W. 1941. Stratigraphic terminology. *Bull. Geol. Soc. Amer.* vol. 52, pp. 1419–1426.

SCHINDEWOLF, O. H. 1963. Neokatastrophismus? *Zeitschr. Deutsch. Geol. Ges.* vol. 114, pp. 430–445.

SCHIRARDIN, J. 1961. Sur la limite du Toarcien et de l'Aalénien en Alsace. *Bull. Carte géol. Alsace & Lorraine* vol. 13, part 3.

SCHUCHERT, C. 1943. *Stratigraphy of the eastern and central United States.* New York: John Wiley.

SEDGWICK, A. *in* SEDGWICK, A. & MURCHISON, R. I. 1835. On the Silurian and Cambrian Systems . . . *London & Edin. Phil. Mag.* vol. 7, p. 484. [Also *Rep. Brit. Ass. Adv. Sci.*, part 2, pp. 59–61].

SEDGWICK, A. & MURCHISON, R. I. 1839. On the classification of the older rocks of Devon and Cornwall. *Proc. Geol. Soc. Lond.* vol. 3, pp. 121–123.

SHROCK, R. R. 1948. *Sequence in layered rocks.* New York: McGraw-Hill.

SPATH, L. F. 1942. The ammonite zones of the Lias. *Geol. Mag.* vol. 79, pp. 264–268.

STAMP, L. D. 1920. Note on the determination of the limit between the Silurian and Devonian Systems. *Geol. Mag.* vol. 57, pp. 164–171.

STRACHEY, J. 1719. A curious description of the strata observed in the coal-mines of Mendip in Somersetshire. *Phil. Trans. Roy. Soc.* vol. 30, pp. 968–973.

STRAW, S. H. 1930. The Siluro-Devonian boundary in South-Central Wales. *Jour. Manchester Geol. Ass.* vol. 1, pp. 79–102.

STRUTT, R. J. 1908. On the accumulation of helium in geological time. *Proc. Roy. Soc. Lond.* ser. A, vol. 81, pp. 272–277.

STUBBLEFIELD, C. J. & TROTTER, F. M. 1957. Divisions of the Coal Measures on Geological Survey maps of England and Wales. *Bull. Geol. Surv. G.B.* no. 13, pp. 1–5.

TARLO, L. B. H. 1964. Siluro-Devonian boundary *in* Psammosteiformes (Agnatha): a review with descriptions of new material from the Lower Devonian of Poland. *Paleont. Polonica* no. 13, pp. 70–72.

TEICHERT, C. 1957. Discussion of Report 5—Nature, usage and nomenclature of biostratigraphic nomenclature: American Commission on Stratigraphic Nomenclature. *Bull. Amer. Ass. Petrol. Geol.* vol. 41, pp. 2574–2575.

—— 1958. Some biostratigraphical concepts. *Bull. Geol. Soc. Amer.* vol. 69, pp. 99–120.

THOMSON, J. E. 1953. Problems of Precambrian stratigraphy west of Sudbury, Ontario. *Trans. Roy. Soc. Canada* vol. 47, ser. 3, section 4, pp. 61–70.

TOMKEIEFF, S. I. 1963. Unconformity—an historical study. *Proc. Geol. Ass.* vol. 73, pp. 383–417.

TRUEMAN, A. E. 1946. Anniversary Address: Stratigraphical problems in the Coal Measures of Europe and North America. *Quart. Jour. Geol. Soc. Lond.* vol. 102, pp. xlix–xciii.

UDDEN, J. A. 1924. Laminated anhydrite in Texas. *Bull. Geol. Soc. Amer.* vol. 35, pp. 347–354.

VAN HISE, C. R. 1908. The problem of the Pre-Cambrian. *Bull. Geol. Soc. Amer.* vol. 19, pp. 1–28.

VAUGHAN, A. 1905. The palaeontological sequence in the Carboniferous Limestone of the Bristol area. *Quart. Jour. Geol. Soc. Lond.* vol. 61, pp. 181–307.

—— 1915. Correlation of Dinantian and Avonian. *Quart. Jour. Geol. Soc. Lond.* vol. 71, pp. 1–52.

WANLESS, H. R. & SHEPARD, F. P. 1936. Sea level and climatic changes related to late Paleozoic cycles. *Bull. Geol. Soc. Amer.* vol. 47, pp. 1177–1206.

WANLESS, H. R. & WELLER, J. M. 1932. Correlation and extent of Pennsylvanian cyclothems. *Bull. Geol. Soc. Amer.* vol. 43, pp. 1003–1016.

WELCH, F. B. A. & TROTTER, F. M. 1961. Geology of the country around Monmouth and Chepstow. *Mem. Geol. Surv. G.B.*

WHITE, E. I. 1950. The vertebrate faunas of the Lower Old Red Sandstone of the Welsh Borders. *Bull. Brit. Mus. (Nat. Hist.), Geol.* vol. 1, part 3, pp. 49–89.

WILLIAMS, H. S. 1901. The discrimination of time-values in geology. *Jour. Geol.* vol. 9, pp. 570–585.

WILLMARTH, M. G. 1925. The geologic time classification of the United States Geological Survey compared with other classifications. Accompanied by the original definitions of era, period and epoch terms. *Bull. U.S. Geol. Surv.* no. 769.

WOOD, H. E. *et al.* 1941. Nomenclature and correlation of the North American continental Tertiary. *Bull. Geol. Soc. Amer.* vol. 52, pp. 1–48.

WOODFORD, A. O. 1963. Correlation by fossils. *The fabric of geology* edited by C. A. Albritton. Stanford, Calif. pp. 75–111.

WOODLAND, A. W., EVANS, W. B. & STEPHENS, J. V. 1957. Classification of the Coal Measures of South Wales with special reference to the Upper Coal Measures. *Bull. Geol. Surv. G.B.* no. 13, pp. 6–13.

WRIGHT, W. B. 1926. Stratigraphical diachronism in the Millstone Grit of Lancashire. *Rep. Brit. Ass. Adv. Sci.* (Oxford, 1926), pp. 354–355.

YOUNG, K. 1963. Upper Cretaceous ammonites from the Gulf Coast of the United States. *Univ. Texas Publ.* no. 6304.

INDEX

Bold type indicates pages on which terms are defined or explained.